BEHAVIORAL SCIENCE IN INDUSTRY SERIES

Edited by Victor H. Vroom
Yale University

☐ = II

Man-Machine Engineering

Alphonse Chapanis

The Johns Hopkins University

Brooks/Cole Publishing Company

Monterey, California
A Division of Wadsworth Publishing Company, Inc.

Tavistock Publications, Ltd.

London

To Natasha

15   14   13

L.C. Cat. Card No.: 65–15099
Printed in the United States of America

Published simultaneously in Great Britain by Tavistock Publications, Ltd., London

foreword

The heterogeneity of behavioral science in industry makes it impossible for a single author to do justice to the subject's many facets in a single text. Although full-length volumes on particular topics are available for the specialist, these books are often beyond the level of the advanced undergraduate or beginning graduate student, and they typically go into more detail than is justified in a general course. To meet the changing educational needs generated by this complex subject matter, the Behavioral Science in Industry series was conceived.

The concept is simple. Leading authorities have written short books, at a fairly basic level, to present the essentials of particular fields of inquiry. These books are designed to be used in combination, as a basic text for courses in industrial psychology or behavioral science in industry, or singly, as supplementary texts or collateral reading in more specialized courses.

To implement this concept, the editor outlined the general scope of the series, specified a list of titles, and sketched the content of each volume. Leading social scientists nominated authors for each of the proposed books, and, in following up these leads, the editor was extremely fortunate in enlisting the enthusiastic cooperation of the kinds of men who are not only specialists in their subjects, but who can communicate their ideas in highly readable fashion.

The need for such a series is apparent from the marked changes that have occurred in the last two or three decades in the application of the scientific method to the study of human behavior at work. Perhaps the most significant of these changes is the extension of the range of problems subjected to systematic research. The continuing concern of industrial psychology with methods of assessing individual differences for the selection and placement of personnel has been supplemented by intensive research on such diverse topics as leadership and supervision, the design of man-machine systems, consumer preferences, management development, career patterns, and union-management relations.

This expanding focus of industrial psychology has been accompanied by changes in the objectives and strategies of research. Research has become less concerned with techniques for solving particular problems and more concerned with shedding light on the processes that underlie various behavioral phenomena, on the assumption that improvements in technology will be facilitated by a better understanding of these processes. To implement these new objectives, the psychometric and correlational methods of research in personnel selection and placement were adapted to new problems and supplemented by experiments in laboratory and field settings. As a result, the study of behavior in industrial organizations has been undertaken by researchers who have not previously been identified with industrial psychology. Experimental psychologists investigated problems of human factors in equipment design; social psychologists worked on problems of leadership, communication, and social influence; and clinical psychologists applied their diagnostic and therapeutic skills in industrial settings.

The net effect has been a blurring of the boundary lines among these subdisciplines and a growing recognition of the interdependence of "basic" and "applied" research. These changes have also obscured lines of demarcation among disciplines and professions. Psychologists, sociologists, cultural anthropologists, political scientists, and economists, and specialists in such functional managerial fields as production, labor relations, marketing, and accounting have discovered that much of their work is interrelated and that their interests are often mutual. The resultant cross-fertilization has given an interdisciplinary character to much of the new research and has afforded some currency to the interdisciplinary label *behavioral science.*

This series has been planned to reflect these changes in subject matter and research methods and to provide the reader with a valuable summary of the current status of behavioral science in industry.

Victor H. Vroom

preface

In the twenty years that have elapsed since World War II, human factors engineering and its subordinate field, engineering psychology, have shown phenomenal growth. There are many numbers that can be used to quantify the development of a new technology: the number of people who practice it, the number of industries that use it, the number of professional societies that represent it, or the number of articles and books that are written in it. By any of these criteria, engineering psychology today exhibits extraordinary vigor.

In 1945, there were no books specifically concerned with human factors engineering. The book *Applied Experimental Psychology,* published in 1949, was the first of its kind. Today we have a score or more textbooks to choose from. But one thing we have not had till now is a little book, a book for the general reader. In *Man-Machine Engineering,* that is what I have tried to write.

My aim in writing this book has been to convey the flavor of the field. I've tried to give some insight into why man-machine mismatchings occur, how engineering psychologists go about discovering solutions to these problems, and what some of these solutions are. Above all, I've tried to write so that an average, nontechnical reader can understand what human engineering is all about.

However hard he works, no author works alone. My writing team included, first, my wife, who, though she did not set a single word to paper, wrote this book with me. I am also indebted to a large number of students, my severest critics, for listening to some parts of the book, for reading other parts of it, and for giving frank comments on all of it. One of these students, George White, read the final manuscript meticulously from beginning to end. His insightful and detailed criticisms were responsible for revealing some woeful obscurities. Finally, my secretary, Margaret Iwata, patiently fetched my coffee, shielded me from the outside world during the book's composition, and typed, and typed, and typed. To all of these I owe more than I can ever express in writing.

Alphonse Chapanis

contents

Introduction

At one minute after nine on the morning of June 30, 1956, Trans World Airlines' Flight 2, a regularly scheduled passenger service, took off from Los Angeles International Airport with Kansas City, Missouri, as its destination. It was followed three minutes later by United Air Lines' Flight 718, a regularly scheduled service from Los Angeles to Chicago, Illinois.

Both planes were the most advanced types in use for commercial transport at the time. The TWA plane, a Super-Constellation, had received a periodic maintenance check at Los Angeles and was in good condition. The UAL DC-7 had also been checked at Los Angeles. Both flight engineers performed preflight and walkaround inspections of their respective aircraft before take-off. All the crew members on both aircraft were experienced, rested, in good physical condition, and certified for their positions. Captain Gandy, commander of the Super-Constellation, was a well-qualified veteran of nearly 15,000 flying hours, a man who had flown the route from Los Angeles to Kansas City approximately 177 times. Captain Shirley, commander of the DC-7, was equally well qualified and had even more flying experience than Captain Gandy.

The flight plan for TWA 2 specified a cruising altitude of 19,000 feet; that for UAL 718 specified 21,000 feet. Twenty minutes after take-off, TWA 2 requested a change in altitude assignment from 19,000 to 21,000 feet. The Los Angeles Air Route Traffic Controller denied this request because of traffic (UAL's Flight 718) at that altitude. Flight 2 then submitted a request to fly "1,000 feet on top," that is, 1,000 feet above the nearest cloud cover. After determining that the flight was already at least 1,000 feet on top, ARTC cleared this change but warned TWA 2 about United 718's flight in the vicinity. Captain Gandy heard and acknowledged this message.

At approximately 9:58 the Civil Aeronautics Administration communications station at Needles, California, received a routine position report. "United 718, over Needles at 9:58; 21,000, estimating Painted Desert at '31." One minute later there was another routine report, through TWA company radio at Las Vegas. "TWA 2, passed Lake Mohave at 9:55; 1,000 on top at 21,000, estimating Painted Desert 10:31."

At 10:31, Aeronautical Radio communicators at Salt Lake City and San Francisco picked up a garbled radio transmission. Speech experts at Bell Telephone Laboratories later analyzed the taped message and discovered two voices. One was that of a man yelling, ". . . UP . . . UP." The other was that of First Officer Harms, reporting for the last time: "Salt Lake, United 718 . . . ah . . . we're going in."

The wreckage, with its cargo of 128 human bodies, was discovered strewn for over a mile along the depths of the Grand Canyon.

With the help of Army helicopters, Civil Aeronautics Board investigators were on the scene the next day. The investigation that followed was detailed, difficult, and hazardous. Every dent, scratch, tear, bend, smear of rubber, and smudge of paint was carefully identified and studied. Slowly a consistent picture emerged. Concave areas on the Super-Constellation's empennage fitted together precisely with the damage on the DC-7's wingtip. Red paint from the DC-7's wing matched exactly paint smears on the fuselage of the Super-Constellation. Black marks from the deicer boot on one plane coincided with rubber smears on the other. A section of the undersurface of the DC-7's left wing was found some distance from the main part of the wreckage. Imbedded in the wing fragment was a piece of fabric torn from the ceiling of the Super-Constellation's cabin.

In the end, the weight of all the evidence was so conclusive that there could be little doubt about what had happened. The DC-7 had approached from above and behind at an angle 5 to 10 degrees from the Super-Constellation. Its left wing had struck the upper-aft fuselage of the Super-Constellation with disintegrating force, and, as the aircraft continued to pass laterally, the leading edge of the Super-Constellation's left tail fin made contact with the left wingtip of the DC-7, tearing off pieces of both components. Meanwhile, the No. 1 propeller of the DC-7 slashed rhythmically into the Super-Constellation's rear baggage compartment. This entire sequence, CAB investigators estimated, took place in less than one-half second.

The CAB report concludes ". . . that the probable cause of this mid-air collision was that the pilots did not see each other in time . . ." Figure 1–1 shows how this disaster might have occurred (3).

FIGURE 1–1. *Poor visibility to the rear and below probably caused the Grand Canyon crash. Although the exact positions of the two aircraft are not known, this drawing shows how the limited fields of vision from the converging DC-7 (behind) and Super-Constellation could have prevented each pilot from seeing the other plane until too late. The triangles show the approximate fields of vision from each airliner.*

Men versus Machines

Although the Grand Canyon accident was more tragic than most, it is only one of hundreds of accidents that occur daily in our homes, on our streets, in our schools and factories, on our seas, and in the air. Especially important is the fact that it is a kind of accident that is occurring ever more frequently. For it was the result of a relatively new kind of conflict in our civilization—a conflict between men and the machines they operate. Let us look more closely at the issue in this case.

Pilot Visibility—a Human Factor

When the intrepid aviator of fifty years ago soared into the air, he sat in the open and enjoyed a magnificent view. He could see the earth below, to the right, the left, and even to the rear. Above, the sky reached out limitlessly. To be sure, there were some obstructions in his field of view—the fuselage in front, the wings to the sides, and the control surfaces behind. But it was a rare aircraft that did not allow the pilot to see nine-tenths of the space around him.

In the decades that followed, the speed of aircraft increased, their contours became more streamlined, the pilot was pushed back behind a console covered with dials, gauges, switches, knobs, and other gadgets. And the pilot became more remote from the space through which he flew. The pilot of a Super-Constellation can see less than one-eighth of the space around him; the pilot of a DC-7, scarcely 10 per cent. (See Fig. 1–2.)

Transport pilots have long complained about the shrinking visibility from the craft they fly. Indeed, they find it almost impossible to see another airplane even when it is right alongside. The wonder is that there have been so few mid-air collisions—only 168 mid-air collisions involving civil aircraft have been recorded in this country over the ten-year period from 1952 through 1961. A much more disturbing and realistic indication of the potential danger is the number of near misses in which good luck or fast evasive action on the part of pilots prevented still more tragedies. In a single year (from July 1, 1961, to June 30, 1962) pilots reported to the Flight Safety Foundation (13) a total of 2,577 near mid-air collisions over the territory of the United States. This is an average of more than seven a day!

What lesson can we draw from this story? It is this: The machine we call an aircraft handicaps its human operator because of the way it is designed.

Still More Evidence

If you are sensitive to the conflict between men and machines, and are alert to the problems it creates, you can read between the lines of many newspaper stories to collect more evidence. For example, on September 6, 1956, the year of the Grand Canyon crash, newspaper headlines revealed that twenty people were killed and thirty-five injured when the Santa Fe Chief ran into a parked mail train near Springer, New Mexico. A railway spokesman stated that the fireman on the mail train had become confused and set the switch on the main track incorrectly.

FIGURE 1–2. *Cockpit of a modern jet airliner. Note the restricted forward visibility available to the pilot (left) and co-pilot (right). Note, too, the assemblage of dials, indicators, and controls which these men must monitor and use. The flight engineer (right forward) uses an even larger number of displays and controls, but these are not shown here.*

Later that same year, on December 24, 1956, the Washington, D.C., *Post* carried a story about a compromise settlement between the Water Department and the Dupont Plaza Hotel for $12,569.67. Over a period of more than seven years—from July 1948, until December 1955—a meter reader had consistently misread the dials in the basement of the hotel. This error resulted in the hotel's being charged for only a tenth of the water it had consumed during this period. The settlement meant a loss of some $8,000 in revenues to the District Water Department.

In March 1962 a shocked nation read that six infants had died in the maternity ward of the Binghamton, New York, General Hospital because they had been fed formulas prepared with salt instead of sugar. The error was traced to a practical nurse who had inadvertently filled a sugar container with salt from one of two identical, shiny, 20-gallon containers standing side by side, under a low shelf, in dim light, in the hospital's main kitchen. A small paper tag pasted to the lid of one container bore the word "Sugar" in plain handwriting. The tag on the other lid was torn, but one could make out the letters "S . . . lt" on the fragments that remained. As one hospital board member put it, "Maybe that girl did mistake salt for sugar, but if so we set her up for it just as surely as if we'd set a trap."

Incidents such as these are dramatic and attention arresting because they are out of the ordinary. But the most obvious illustration of the man-machine conflict that plagues modern civilization is so familiar that we scarcely pay attention to it. About 41,000 people die every year in the United States in street and highway accidents. About 1,500,000 more are injured. The annual cost to the nation of our highway-accident toll has been estimated at a staggering $7,300,000,000. Such frightening statistics should be more than enough to convince us that we do indeed have a man-machine conflict in our society.

Confusion in the Household—and Elsewhere

Not all instances of this conflict are hair-raising or tragic. In fact, many are not accidents at all. Some—like trying to figure out how the heater on your car works—merely add to the countless irritations and frustrations that beset us constantly. Some are even amusing.

Take a look at your electric meter, gas meter, or water meter. Does it look like one of those in Figure 1–3? Can you read it? These dials violate two important psychological principles: (a) Dials are read most easily if the numbers increase in a clockwise direction around the dial. (b) On multiple-dial displays the direction of increase should be consistent throughout.

During World War II, when there was a shortage of meter readers, some utility companies asked householders to read their own meters. The results were so chaotic that this idea was quickly abandoned.

Thereafter, some utility companies provided cards with blank dials printed on them and instructions on how to draw in the positions of the needles. The cards were to be mailed back to the company, where the meter reading was made from the drawings. This kind of card is still used in some cities to get meter readings from householders whenever the meter reader cannot get into a house to read the meter.

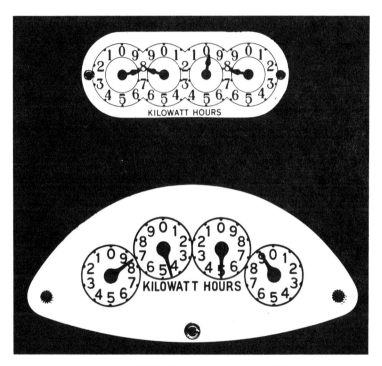

FIGURE 1-3.   *Dials from two types of kilowatt-hour meters in common use. Can you read the indications?*

But surely you must remember exclaiming at some time or other, "What a stupid way to build this thing! Now if they had only put this gadget here instead of there—or done this instead of that—it would have been so much easier to use." The object of your complaint might have been almost anything—your stove, automobile, television set, or power mower. If you have ever been impelled into such an outburst, you have already been introduced to the field of *human factors engineering.*

Human Factors Engineering

Human factors engineering, or human engineering, is concerned with ways of designing machines, operations, and work environments so that they match human capacities and limitations. Another way of saying this is that we shall be concerned in this book with the engineering of machines for human use and with the engineering of human tasks for operating machines.

The Outlook of the Human Factors Engineer

The basic philosophy of the human factors engineer is perhaps most easily understood by thinking about the accidents, errors, and problems that introduced this chapter. For years it has been customary to write off most aircraft accidents as the result of "pilot error." In fact, the saying "To err is human" is so ingrained in everyday speech and thinking that it has frankly misled us for a long time. Accident statistics compiled by insurance companies on home, street, railway, and industrial accidents are full of *causes* such as *carelessness, faulty attitude,* and *inattention.* Although labels such as these *appear* to tell us something, they really don't. Everyone is inattentive at some time or other, and to say that an accident was caused by inattentiveness gives us no clue whatsoever about how we could have prevented it.

Human factors engineers are the first to grant that people make mistakes. But they raise these important questions also: Is some of the blame to be found in the design of the equipment that people use? Do people make more mistakes with some kinds of equipment or vehicles than with others? Is it possible to redesign machines so that human errors are reduced or even eliminated? Research over the past few decades provides us with a resounding "Yes!" to all these questions. This, then, is the rationale behind the approach of the human factors engineer: he starts with the certain knowledge and conviction that people are fallible and careless, and that they have human limitations, but he then turns to the machine and the job to see whether he can eliminate their error-provocative features.

Other Goals of Human Factors Engineering

Our emphasis on accidents and errors in the discussion so far should not leave you with the impression that human factors engineering is synonymous with safety engineering. Increasing safety, and decreasing accidents, is a major goal of human factors engineering, to be sure; but there are other important goals as well. Increasing the efficiency with which machines can be operated, increasing productivity in industrial operations, decreasing the amount of effort required to operate machines, and increasing human comfort in man-machine systems—all these constitute the major objectives of human engineering.

Historical Beginnings

It is correct to say that people have been engaged in human factors engineering of a sort for as long as man has been fashioning tools and implements. Nonetheless, as a separate technology, human factors engineering has a relatively short history. It was not until the end of the nineteenth century that systematic investigations were conducted on the ways in which man's capacity to work is influenced by his job and his tools. In 1898, Frederick W. Taylor made empirical studies to discover the best designs of shovels and the optimum weight per shovelful for handling products such as sand, slag, rice coal, and iron ore. Taylor's interests, however, were primarily in work rates and in the effects of incentives and worker motivation on work rates.

It remained for Frank B. Gilbreth to set a pattern for this field with his classic study of bricklaying in 1911. Among other things, Gilbreth invented a scaffold that could be quickly raised or lowered so that the bricklayer could work at the most convenient level at all times. A shelf held the bricks and mortar at their most convenient positions. By making changes in the transportation and inspection of the bricks, and in their arrangement on the scaffold, Gilbreth enabled bricklayers to increase the number of bricks that they could lay, from 120 to 350 per man per hour. These pioneering studies by Taylor and Gilbreth were the beginning of that branch of industrial engineering now known as *time-and-motion study*.

In the years that followed, time-and-motion engineers developed a number of principles of motion economy, of arrangement of work, and of work design—principles that have been applied throughout modern industry. Insofar as they have been concerned with the redesign of the task, the machine, or the work environment, time-and-motion engineers are predecessors of the modern human factors engineer.

Still, the primary emphasis in time-and-motion engineering has been on man as a worker; that is, as a source of mechanical power. It was not until World War II that a new category of machines appeared —machines that made demands not upon the operator's muscular power, but upon his sensory, perceptual, judgmental, and decision-making abilities. The job of a radar operator, for example, requires virtually no muscular effort, but makes severe demands on sensory capacity, vigilance, and decision-making ability. This new class of machines raised some intricate and unusual questions about human abilities: How much information can a man absorb from a radar screen? How much optical distortion is tolerable in the windscreen of a high-speed aircraft flying low-level strafing missions? What happens if a human operator is suddenly decompressed when the walls of a pressurized aircraft rupture? What are the optimum time constants to build into a rate-aided gunnery tracking system? Can a man withstand an acceleration of twelve times the force of gravity for fifteen seconds? How many sizes of oxygen mask are required to fit the full range of male faces? These questions could no longer be answered by common sense or by the time-and-motion engineers' principles of motion economy. So, during World War II, a new group of scientific experts turned their efforts to the integration of man into the new and complicated machine systems which were the products of the war effort. These new experts were not engineers but behavioral scientists—psychologists, physiologists, anthropometrists, and physicians. As a result of their influence, human factors engineering emerged as a special discipline.

Current Status of the Field

Following World War II, the growth of human factors engineering has been very rapid. Human factors engineers are now employed in every branch of the military, in many independent research and consulting organizations, and in the aviation, automotive, electronics, communications, and home-appliance industries. The systems and devices with which they work range from space vehicles, digital computers, and automated teaching machines to more ordinary devices such as highway signs, telephones, typewriters, machine tools, and kitchen stoves. In a very real sense, it is the phenomenal growth in the number and complexity of machines in every segment of our industrialized society that has created the need for, and that sustains, the field of human factors engineering.

The Scope of Human Factors Engineering

The information that human factors engineers need in their work comes from all the social and behavioral sciences. The amount of such information that may be used, however, depends on the particular design problem and on the industry. In the design of a space vehicle, almost everything known about man is important: body dimensions; physiological reactions to environmental stresses such as accelerative forces and extreme variations in temperature and atmospheric pressure; sensory capacities in relation to instrument and display indications; the ability to make timely decisions; the ability to make correct control movements; learning, or the modification of behavior through training; eating, drinking, and waste disposal; and the psychological consequences of fatigue, emotion, and isolation. By contrast, the design of a highway sign or the design of a switch for an electric toaster is a much smaller problem, dealing with only a restricted part of man's sensorimotor repertory. For want of space, we shall have to content ourselves in this book with only an introduction to this large field. More complete treatments of the subject matter can be found in books (6, 23, 25) listed in the References.

Engineering Psychology

People who identify themselves as human factors engineers may have come originally from any of the life sciences. But the majority (well over 50 per cent of the members of the Human Factors Society, for example) came into it from psychology—probably because the primary load that modern machines place on their human operators is a *mental* load. So important are the psychological contributions to human factors engineering that a special branch of psychology, *engineering psychology*, has evolved to deal with them. Although engineering psychology is a part of human factors engineering, it is an important part. This book deals primarily with engineering psychology, and with the contributions that psychologists have made to the field of human factors engineering.

A Word about Names

As is often true of new things, people are not entirely sure about what to call this new technology. In the United States, the names *human engineering* and *human factors engineering*—which are, for all practical purposes, synonymous—are preferred. Both refer to the general field of man-machine relationships as we have defined it here. In England and Europe, however, the term *ergonomics* is generally accepted as being identical to *human factors engineering*. Other terms used from time to time are *biotechnology, biomechanics,* and *life-sciences engineering.* These three terms are essentially equivalent to *human factors engineering,* but they are used less commonly in this country.

The subfield of *engineering psychology* has been referred to as *applied experimental psychology, applied psychophysics,* and *psycho-technology.* Although these four names may be considered identical, the term *engineering psychology* is the one used most frequently these days, and so it is to be preferred to the others.

Summary

This chapter has introduced you to the field of human factors engineering and its subfield engineering psychology. We discovered that these fields are concerned with the engineering of machines and with the design of tasks for efficient, safe, and comfortable human operation. Our emphasis is on the contributions that modern psychology has made to the solution of these problems. The chapter traces the history of the field and suggests why it has become so important today. We have defined the scope of these areas of specialization and closed with a discussion of some of the names that are used to refer to them. In the next chapter we take a closer look at man-machine systems and the role that man plays in them.

chapter two

Man in
Man-Machine
Systems

Turn to the advertisements in a large number of professional journals, or to the classified ads of many metropolitan newspapers, and you will be struck by the number of times you come across the words *systems engineer* and *systems engineering*. Now look through the same journals and newspapers of twenty or thirty years ago, and you will hardly find these words at all. The concept of *systems*—though not completely new in engineering—is a relative newcomer to our every-day technical vocabularies. Among the special sorts of systems that are being talked about more and more these days are *man-machine systems*, the kind with which we are primarily concerned in this book.

What is a system? What kind of system is a man-machine system? What kinds of things does man do, and what should he do, in a man-machine system? These are the specific questions we shall wrestle with in this chapter.

What Is a System?

The word *system* is used in many different ways, and it means different things to different people. So we may speak of the solar *system*, the capitalistic *system*, a *system* for betting on horses, or the nervous *system* of the human body—just to take a few examples. In this book, however, we are concerned only with *equipment* systems. With this in mind, then, we may define a system as *a group of com-*

ponents—at least some of which are pieces of equipment—designed to work together for some common purpose.

Some common examples of systems are the bicycle, the automobile, and the airplane. They all fit our definition because:

1. They consist of a number of pieces of equipment.
2. The pieces of equipment are designed to fit together and work together.
3. The entire assemblage of equipment has, in each case, been designed with a common purpose in view.

Note, too, that although these are all vehicles of transportation, they are of vastly different orders of complexity. A bicycle is a fairly simple system; an airplane is a highly complex one.

Some other systems, of varying degrees of complexity, are:

1. A telephone switchboard.
2. The telephone system of the United States.
3. The railroad system of the United States.
4. A student working with a teaching machine.
5. An air-to-ground missile system.
6. A radar operator working with radar.
7. The air-traffic-control system of the United States.
8. A manufacturing plant.

The Origin of Systems

In the early days of our industrial civilization, machines were simple extensions of man's muscles: tools, construction devices, vehicles, catapults, and the like. There were, of course, some instruments, such as microscopes and telescopes, designed to increase the range of man's senses; but by and large the most important function that early machines served was that of amplifying man's muscular power. Somewhat later, in the early days of the industrial revolution, many machines were assembled and sometimes connected together in a variety of ways to make our first large-scale systems, the factories. Lathes, milling machines, and power presses were laid out on a concrete floor, overhead shafts and pulleys were installed to provide power to each machine, and a conveyor threaded in and around the various machines to bring in raw materials and take away the finished products.

When several small systems or machines were simply joined together to make a big one, however, unforeseen difficulties often arose. Even though the machine elements were individually adequate, very often they did not work together as a whole. The problems of combining separate components into a system are well illustrated by the telephone system. It is not enough that a switching circuit, a telephone switchboard, or a telephone handset be designed as a single unit. Instead, each new circuit and each new piece of equipment must fit into and be compatible with the entire telephone network. For this reason, each new circuit and each new item of equipment has to be tested not only as a unit but in conjunction with many other circuits that already exist, or—and this is a point that must not be overlooked—with circuits that might be planned for the future.

The increasing growth of large systems has created other problems as well. To build a system as complex as a telephone system may require a score or more of different specialists: electrical, mechanical, civil, and chemical engineers; mathematicians; physicists; economists; psychologists; and architects. These specialists use their own particular methods, devices, and words, and they often find it difficult to communicate with one another. Moreover, they are often so engrossed with the intricacies and minutiae of their specific jobs that they see problems only from their own perspective and lose sight of the overall plan and purpose of the system.

Problems such as these make it apparent that we need new concepts and new methods to deal with the many large systems that are becoming part of our everyday lives. We also need engineering generalists who can maintain a very broad outlook—men who can see the forest as well as the trees. Such men are the systems engineers, and their method of tackling problems is that of systems engineering.

Systems within Systems

Systems may be virtually any size, and any given system usually exists as a part of other systems. A telephone operator using a telephone switchboard is an example of a small system. But this small system is just a tiny element in the much larger system of a central telephone station. The latter is in turn but a small component of an appreciably greater system, the telephone system of the United States. The size of a system is arbitrary; the amount of the system that may be delineated and worked on at any time depends to a considerable extent on what is convenient or appears to be appropriate at the moment.

Man-Machine Systems

People are used or involved in every equipment system, because equipment systems are always built for some *human* purpose. They exist to serve some human need. In addition, systems are designed and built by people. Further, it is humans who monitor—who keep an eye on, supervise, and maintain—the systems. Systems do not replace their own burned-out vacuum tubes, transistors, or light bulbs, or solder their own connections. People do all these things. For these reasons, one could argue that all equipment systems are man-machine systems. Nonetheless, systems vary enormously in the degree to which they involve human operators in any active sense. The system of traffic lights that regulates the traffic flow of any large city operates independently of human operators. Once the lights and regulating mechanism are installed, the lights go on and off automatically. In systems of this type, the role of the human being is largely that of designer, builder, and maintenance man. In contrast, the automobile is a good example of a highly complex system in which the operator plays a commanding role or actively intervenes in the system from time to time. An automobile can run for a considerable time without an operator, but to serve its primary purpose as a conveyance to take something or somebody from here to there, the direct, continual interaction of a human operator is absolutely essential. The automobile is a first-rate example of a true man-machine system.

To come to a definition, then, we may say that *a man-machine system is an equipment system in which at least one of the components is a human being who interacts with or intervenes in the operation of the machine components of the system from time to time.*

Because of newspaper stories and headlines that tell us about the wonders of automation, it is easy to get the idea that automatic machines work entirely on their own. The fact is that many automatic systems use human operators in one way or another. Indeed, it is easy to overlook or to be misled about the amount of work that human operators do in automatic systems. The proportion of men to each machine unit is steadily decreasing, and operators have to learn new kinds of skills in order to operate our modern systems. But operators are often still there, actively participating in the operation of many so-called automatic systems today.

Human Factors in the Development of Systems

The human problems involved in the development of complex systems can be grouped into two general classes. First are the problems directly concerned with designing the system and its machine components so that they best complement the capacities and limitations of the human beings who will work in the system. This class of problems, in modern system work, is sometimes referred to as the *hardware subsystem*. Once a system is designed, however, there is another class of problems, specifically concerned with the procurement, selection, classification, training, and promotion of the people who work in the system. This group of problems is sometimes referred to as the *personnel subsystem*. In this book, we are concerned only with the first of these problems.

The distinction between these two classes of problems, however, is by no means clear-cut. Indeed, work in both areas often goes on simultaneously, or very nearly so, in the development of a system. A well-known, and dramatic, illustration is the space-exploration program of the United States. The first seven astronauts were carefully selected and given extensive training long before the first space capsule was built. In fact, it would have been of little use to have completed a space capsule, its booster, and associated equipment if there was no one ready to fly it.

These two classes of human problems are related in still another respect. A machine's design largely dictates the kinds of people who will be selected to operate it and the amount of training they will need before they can go to work. Conversely, when a job requires a level of aptitude or skill that is difficult to find, one solution to the problem is to redesign the machine or operation so that it can be handled by more ordinary people after a shorter period of training. The recent developments in simplified programming for giant digital computers is an example of this kind of interaction.

Allocation of Tasks to Men and Machines

In preparing his plans for a complex system, the systems engineer begins with decisions about the functions that will be performed by the different parts of the system. Throughout his plans, he keeps in mind that the separate parts must cooperate effectively.

MACHINE FUNCTIONS

Insofar as the machine parts of the system are concerned, the systems engineer makes his decisions partly on the basis of what can and cannot be done with machines at the present time. These decisions vary with time. Twenty years ago, it would have been impossible for a systems designer seriously to consider designing for banks an accounting system in which checks were sorted and bank balances computed and printed automatically by machine. Today such systems are not only feasible but actually in operation. On the other hand, it would be impossible for a systems designer today seriously to consider designing for banks an accounting system in which the amount of each check is read or signatures are verified automatically by machine. There are no machines available at the present time, or in the immediate future, capable of reading all the different kinds of handwriting that appear on checks (see Fig. 2–1). Instead, the task of reading the amount of a check must be done by human operators and converted by them into a machine-readable form. After that, the operation can be finished automatically by machine. Twenty years from now, however, even this part of the accounting operation may be performed by machine, because much effort is currently being devoted to devising machines that can "recognize" handwriting.

ROLE OF MEN

A greatly oversimplified but useful way of looking at the role of man in man-machine systems is illustrated in Figure 2–2. Basically, man has first to sense something and to perceive what this something means. The thing he senses is usually some sort of machine *display*. A display may be any of a thousand or more things—the position of a pointer on a dial, the readout of a digital computer, a sound from a loudspeaker, a red light flashing on a control panel, or the feel of a certain kind of control. Having sensed the display, the man has to interpret it, understand it, perhaps do some mental computation, and reach a decision. In so doing, the operator often uses another important human ability—his ability to remember, to compare what he perceives with his past experiences, to recall operating rules that he learned during training, or to coordinate what he perceives with the strategies he may have formed for handling similar events. He is not necessarily aware that he is doing these things. His behavior may be so well practiced or routine that his decisions may be made almost reflexly, just as the experienced driver may decide almost unconsciously whether to stop or not when he sees a green traffic light change to yellow. In textbooks of psychology, these functions are often discussed under the

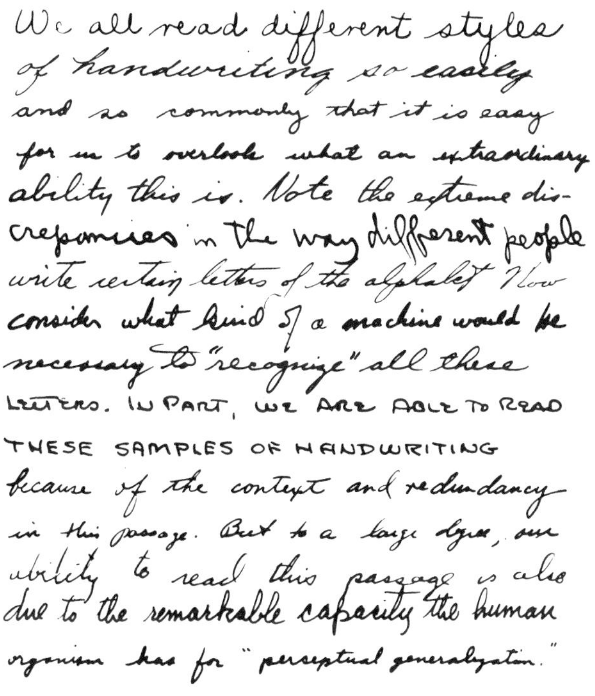

We all read different styles of handwriting so easily and so commonly that it is easy for us to overlook what an extraordinary ability this is. Note the extreme discrepancies in the way different people write certain letters of the alphabet. Now consider what kind of a machine would be necessary to "recognize" all these LETTERS. IN PART, WE ARE ABLE TO READ THESE SAMPLES OF HANDWRITING because of the context and redundancy in this passage. But to a large degree, our ability to read this passage is also due to the remarkable capacity the human organism has for "perceptual generalization."

FIGURE 2–1. *Human beings far surpass machines in perceptual capacities. In fact, human operators often must be deliberately designed into man-machine systems because of their perceptual capacities.*

heading of *higher mental processes.* Today it is the fashion to use machine terminology instead of more ordinary psychological terms; and, in keeping with this trend, Figure 2–2 refers to these higher mental processes collectively as *data processing.*

After having reached his decision, the human operator normally takes some action. This action is usually exercised on some sort of control—a pushbutton, lever, crank, pedal, switch, or handle. Man's action upon these controls in turn exerts an influence on the behavior of the machine, its output, and displays. These functions are performed in a working environment that may seriously affect the operator, the machine, or both. The list of these environmental factors is long, and Figure 2–2 suggests only a few of the more important ones.

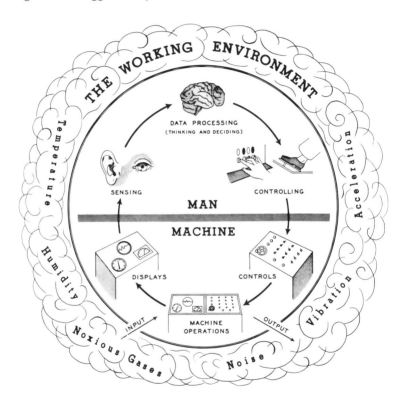

FIGURE 2–2. *Simplified model of a man-machine system.*

Designing for Man-Machine Compatibility

In all three categories of functions described above—sensing, higher mental functioning, and controlling—man's efficiency, speed, and accuracy are profoundly affected by the design of the machine components with which he works. One essential task of the human factors engineer is to design machine displays, controls, and working environment so that they are most compatible with man's natural abilities. The rest of this book is a discussion of ways in which this compatibility can be achieved. But first let us look at this idea of man-machine compatibility a little more closely and see in what way the systems designer can influence the efficiency of a man-machine combination by his design of tasks for men. Three examples—one to illustrate each of the three general human functions we have been discussing above—should clarify the problem.

CHOOSING THE CORRECT SENSORY CHANNEL

In most cases, the systems engineer has considerable latitude in designing individual components. Suppose that the output of a machine is a series of electrical pulses. These may be connected to any of a large number of display elements. For instance, electrical pulses may be used to make a light flash or a buzzer sound intermittently. Moreover, construction of either of these displays is a simple engineering job. Which should the designer use? The answer is that he should use the form of display that is most compatible with the job the man has to do. If, for example, the man has to count these pulses quickly, the pulses should be presented as sounds, since rapidly presented stimuli are more compatible with the auditory sense than with the visual sense. The average person can count up to five "dots" aurally when each is separated by only 125 milliseconds, whereas 500 milliseconds are required if the dots are presented visually, as pulses of light (28, 29). Here, then, is a simple illustration showing how man's sensing function can be helped or hindered by the way the corresponding machine element (the display) is designed.

CHOOSING APPROPRIATE NUMBERING SYSTEMS

To show how man's higher mental processes can be affected by machine design, we turn to an experiment on the estimation of distances of targets on a radar scope. Figure 2-3 is a schematic illustration of the PPI (plan position indicator) on the end of a CRT (cathode-ray tube)—the viewing end of a radar. The center of this display corresponds to the location of the radar. The six short black lines interspersed throughout the display represent targets at various distances and in various directions from the radar. The concentric black circles in the display are *range rings*. One way of estimating the distance of a target from the radar is by interpolating between range rings. Suppose, for example, that the range rings mark off 2.5-mile intervals. This means that the rings—reading from the center out—represent distances of 2.5, 5.0, and 7.5 miles, while the outer edge of the central

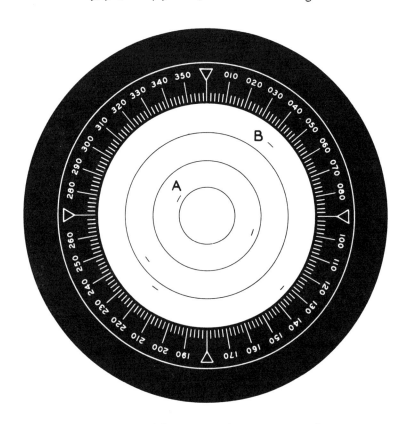

FIGURE 2–3. *The PPI (plan position indicator) of a modern radar. Six targets—two of them labeled A and B—are shown. The concentric circles are range rings that represent increasing distances from the radar, located symbolically at the exact center of the display.*

display area represents a distance of 10.0 miles. You can see that the target labeled *A* in the illustration is about 3 miles away, and the target labeled *B* is about 8.25 miles away.

Another possibility, however, would be to call the range rings

5,000, 10,000, 15,000, and 20,000 yards. This is an interesting alternative because 2.5 nautical miles equals 5,000 yards. Here is a case, then, in which the machine is unchanged, the visual display is the same, and the radar is measuring the same distances. But how well can human operators do visual interpolation with the two kinds of numbering systems? The answer, according to an experiment by Chapanis and Leyzorek (7), is that errors of visual interpolation are nearly twice as large with the 2.5-mile scale as they are with the 5,000-yard scale. This finding illustrates a situation in which the mental functions of estimation and interpolation are affected markedly by the job, even though the information displayed to the senses is, so far as we can tell, precisely the same.

CHOOSING THE PROPER CONTROL

For our last illustration, consider that our human operator has received some information from a machine display, that he has interpreted it and decided that he needs to make a change in a machine setting. The machine setting is displayed by a linear scale and pointer. The position of the pointer could be controlled by either (a) a simple knob or (b) a simple crank of the same size. Which should our designer use? The answer here, according to research by Jenkins and Connor (17), is a simple knob. In this case, the display is the same, the higher mental functions (decisions) are the same, but the speed and accuracy of the operator's movements are affected by the kind of control device he has to use.

QUESTIONS FOR THE SYSTEMS DESIGNER

All the illustrations used above are simple ones, much simpler ones than the systems designer, or the human factors engineer, commonly encounters in practice. But the lesson they convey is valid for problems of any degree of complexity. In making decisions about the machine components of a system, the engineer often has considerable latitude in the components he selects and the way they are designed. By designing machine components in either this way or that, the engineer, in effect, changes the job for the human operator. For this reason, it is important to keep in mind at all times questions like these:

1. If I use this piece of hardware, or if I design it this way, what am I requiring the human operator to do?

2. Should I be asking the human operator to do this task this way?

3. Is there an alternate way of designing this machine component to change the corresponding human task to one which people can do better?

4. Is there an alternate way of designing this machine component, so that the human operator can do his part of the job faster, safer, better?

Human Factors in Automated Systems

Automation is not a single or unified process. From a technical point of view, what is usually meant by *automation* is one or more of the following: (a) an increased use of automatic equipment; (b) a greater mechanization of transfer operations and more combining of work units; (c) the use of multiple, closed-loop feedback systems to regulate entire production processes. The introduction of these techniques has resulted in dramatic changes in modern industry, and this in turn has had important social and economic consequences.

Automation is generally costly, since it requires a capital investment of considerable magnitude. On the other hand, the benefits to industry have been very great. In the manufacturing industries, increased efficiency of operation has meant a reduction in the unit cost of manufactured items. In centralized-control operations, such as those in rail systems, power distribution systems, or business accounting systems, automation has resulted in faster operations, fewer accidents and errors, and more effective central control over scattered or peripheral units. To a considerable extent these economies result from the replacement of relatively high-priced human labor with cheaper machine labor. Automation has meant the abolition of hundreds of thousands of jobs, with resultant strains on the supply of and demand for human labor. All these results are well known. But what is not so well known is the effect of automation on the skills required of the workers who still remain. How does automation affect the nature of human engineering and the basic model of the man-machine relationship represented in Figure 2–2?

HUMAN TASKS IN AUTOMATED SYSTEMS

Although automation has resulted in a net decrease in the number of workers employed, it has also resulted in the creation of some new kinds of jobs. Through the introduction of digital computers into the Internal Revenue Service, for example, the millions of income tax returns the Service receives each year can be processed faster, more accurately, and with fewer people. At the same time, however, literally thousands of people in the Internal Revenue Service have had to be retrained to work effectively with these new machines.

In general, human tasks in fully automated systems can be grouped under three major headings (9):

1. *Setting-up processes.* In continuous-flow processes (in automatic refineries, automatic bakeries, and the like), operators determine the order of operations in response to production requirements and feed these orders into the system. In tape-fed machine-tool operations, human operators read blueprints, work out the sequence of actions that the machines must go through, and punch these onto the control tapes. In business and accounting systems, human operators translate data (checks, orders, income-tax returns) into machine language and program the machines to do the necessary operations on these data.

2. *Operating and monitoring.* Human operators have to supervise machine operations. Someone has to push the ON button, change the tapes, provide new sets of punched cards as required, see that the machines are functioning properly, and take over in emergencies.

3. *Maintenance.* One of the major tasks of human operators in modern automatic systems is that of maintaining the system. Some idea of the importance of this function may be conveyed by the finding of the Air Force that with increased complexity and automaticity maintaining an item of equipment may cost as much as ten times the original cost of the equipment! Maintenance is of two primary types: (a) preventive maintenance and (b) repair of malfunctions. In the former case, human operators have to oil the bearings, clean the working parts, and perform other routine tasks necessary to keep a machine functioning. In repair work, the maintenance technician makes test readings on meters or test equipment, uses particular strategies to diagnose malfunctions, and corrects the source of trouble when it has been located.

THE MAN-MACHINE MODEL APPLIED TO AUTOMATED SYSTEMS

Does the man-machine model proposed in Figure 2–2 apply to automated systems too? Let's look at some illustrations.

An oil refinery. Figure 2–4 shows a photograph of a gas recovery and fractionating unit in a modern oil refinery. This refinery consists of towers, pumps, condensers, and auxiliary equipment. A furnace heats

FIGURE 2–4. *A gas recovery and fractionating unit in a modern oil refinery.* (Courtesy of Humble Oil and Refining Company.)

the product of a fluid, catalytic, cracking operation to a carefully controlled temperature. The partially vaporized mixture of ethane, propane, butanes, and pentanes is separated into individual components for use in gasoline and in chemical syntheses such as the manufacture of synthetic rubber, aviation alkylate, and detergents. The entire operation is controlled from the control house shown in the lower right of the photograph.

Figure 2–5 shows the control console inside the control house. Although operating personnel intervene in the operation only during start-up, shut-down, change-over, or emergency conditions, the basic model of the man-machine relationship shown in Figure 2–2 still applies. The operator receives information from displays, and, as you can see, he has a large array of machine display items to watch. The opera-

FIGURE 2–5. *The graphic control panel in the control house of the automatic oil refinery shown in Figure 2–4.* (Courtesy of Humble Oil and Refining Company.)

tor must interpret this information and make decisions about courses of action he should take. Most of the time his decision is to do nothing. When he does have to take action, however, he has to respond quickly by activating the appropriate controls, which are distributed throughout the control console. Thus, the man-machine cycle is complete.

A tape-controlled machine tool. Figure 2–6 illustrates a tape-controlled milling machine that does automatic, continuous-path, contour milling of two- or three-dimensional shapes without the use of templates or models. As compared with conventional machines, this one yields savings of as much as 75 per cent in the time required to do certain jobs, as much as 80 per cent in tooling costs, and produces pieces that are much more uniform. The tape-control unit and associated computer are shown in the background. Notice that the operator has a control console mounted on a pedestal.

What are the human tasks in the operation of this system? First, of course, is the human work required to prepare the tape that goes

FIGURE 2–6. *The Numeric Keller—a tape-controlled, continuous-path milling machine.* (Courtesy of the Pratt and Whitney Company.)

into this system. A draftsman must modify the original drawing of the piece that is to be made so that the dimensions can be programmed for the machine. Next, a process planner prepares a sheet that lists the dimensional data from the revised drawing, together with additional information about machining sequences, tolerances, machine feeds, and so on. Finally, the tape is punched and verified from this process sheet. All of these steps are taken before the tape reaches the operator shown in Figure 2–6. The operator then has to position the work-piece, install the cutting tool, and put the tape into the control unit. Next he locates the cutter at the correct starting point (using visual displays), selects the operating speed he wants, and pushes the GO button. During the automatic operation, indicators continuously moni-tor the exact position of the cutter on all axes and at every point in the program.

At certain times (determined from the visual indicators), the operator may stop the machine, withdraw the spindle, change the cut-ting tool, return the cutter to the machining position, and resume ma-chining under automatic control. At other times, the operator may stop the cycle and throw a switch to invert the axis of the reference points so that symmetrical, right- and left-hand parts can be cut from the same tape. The operator may on occasion override the automatic controls and continue a job manually. And so, once more, the man-machine loop of Figure 2–2 has been completed.

HUMAN SKILLS IN AUTOMATED SYSTEMS

Paradoxically, in many cases automation has made the worker's job both easier and harder (31). Consider first the work of a skilled machine-tool operator working on a conventional lathe. Assume that he is going to do the fairly straightforward job of turning a taper on the end of a cylindrical piece of metal. He starts with a piece of metal stock, inserts it into the chuck, and fastens it in place. He tests the centering of the piece of metal and makes readjustments in its posi-tion if necessary. Next, he selects a cutting tool, positions it accurately on center, and fastens it into the tool post. He operates the feed lever and turns the compound-rest feed screw by hand to turn the taper. He stops and tests the angle of his taper with a center gauge. If necessary, he continues the turning operation until he has precisely the taper he wants. Finally, he unlocks the chuck, and removes and disposes of the finished piece.

Notice that the skills involved here are precise psychomotor skills, which require a considerable amount of learning. Moreover, these skills must be continually practiced. If they are not, the machinist may find himself getting "rusty," like a tennis player, concert pianist, or typist who has been away from his skill for some time. A tape-controlled machine tool (such as that in Fig. 2–6) replaces much of the muscular work required of the operator and demands much less precise psychomotor skill on his part. In this sense, then, we can say that the automatic operation has made the operator's job easier.

In other respects, the operator's job is made harder by an automatic machine tool. First, the operator does not have much opportunity to practice the precise psychomotor skills he needs for his work. As a result, he may not be able to take over effectively when he is required to do so. Second, when a machinist works on a lathe, there is a simple and direct relationship between what he does and what he sees being done. In automatic processes, this natural compatibility between display and control is often lost. There is an element of arbitrariness involved in automatic machines, in that pushbuttons, levers, and controls have an indirect relationship to the actions they control. Add to all this the fact that in automatic processes the operator often can no longer see the operation. He is remote from it (see, for example, Fig. 2–4) and receives his information from displays that tell him about the process symbolically. These symbols in turn must be interpreted if he wants to find out about the state of the process.

To top it all off, the consequences of an error in an automatic system are usually much greater than in a conventional operation. Because the capital investment required for an automatic installation is very great, down-time, idle-time, or time spent in producing unusable products can be immensely costly. In automatic operations, an incorrect interpretation of an indicator, a minor lapse of memory, a failure to notice a critical signal, or a misunderstanding of instructions may have serious results. Excessive and costly waste of material, great damage, injury, or even loss of life may occur. Nonetheless, the operator must usually make decisions rapidly in a highly abstract situation, deprived of the numerous cues that would normally combine to prevent errors in the more natural and direct situations of everyday life. So great are the demands on the human operator that he may (for example, in civilian air-traffic-control systems) sometimes break down because of the mental stress involved. One task of the human factors engineer is to reduce this mental stress to tolerable and safe levels. On the other hand, the mental load on the operator must not be reduced too much. Having too little to do is just as handicapping as having too much to do.

Summary

Systems engineering and the concept of systems are increasingly important in modern technology. This chapter defines *equipment sys-*

tems and *man-machine systems* and illustrates both with familiar examples. The human factors in man-machine systems fall into two principal classes: (a) the design of the equipment itself and (b) the procurement, selection, training, and promotion of the personnel in the system. In this book we are concerned with the former class of problems. We have discussed man's role in man-machine systems and shown how his efficiency as an operator can be seriously affected by the design of individual machine elements. We found that, although automation has largely reduced the amount of human labor in many processes, the basic features of man-machine interaction are still preserved. Paradoxically, automation has made man's job both easier and harder—easier in terms of the physical work involved, but harder in terms of mental loads.

In discussing man-machine systems, this chapter showed that the first point of interaction between man and machine occurred when man was required to sense machine displays and interpret what he sensed. The following chapter focuses on that process and directs our attention to a special class of machine displays—those that communicate to man through his visual sense.

chapter three

The Visual
Presentation of
Information

We now turn to problems of machine displays—to ways in which machines communicate with people and in which people obtain information from machines. Several sensory channels are available for man-machine communication—vision, hearing, touch, mechanical vibration, sense of rotation, sense of gravity and movement, kinesthesis, pain, temperature, smell, and taste—and they have been exploited in man-machine systems in about that order. In practice, only the first three are used to any great extent; and, for reasons of economy, we shall deal systematically with only the first two.

Human Factors in the Selection of
a Communication System

Many factors influence an engineer's decision to use one form of communication rather than another. Cost, engineering feasibility, and existing communication links are some of the things that enter into his consideration. For our purposes here, however, we shall ask only this question: What are the human factors that are relevant to the selection of a communication system? The answer requires, first, a decision about which sensory-input channel should be used for receiving information from the communication link—that is, whether we should design for human eyes or ears.

Visual versus Aural Communication

The choice of the communication medium between machine and man depends on the type of information to be transmitted, the way it is to be used, the location of the man, the environment in which the man operates, and the nature of the sense organ itself. (For example, our ears, unlike our eyes, can receive information from all directions. Moreover, we can't close our ears the way we close our eyes. These properties make the ear well suited to the reception of warning and emergency signals.) But let's be systematic and list the comparative advantages and disadvantages of visual and auditory communication systems.

VISUAL MEANS OF COMMUNICATION

In general, visual communication systems (television, teletype, radar, written or printed materials, dials, gauges, and so on) are more appropriate when:

1. The message to be transmitted is complex or abstract, or contains technical or scientific terms.

2. The message to be transmitted is long.

3. The message needs to be referred to later. (Visual means of communication lend themselves well to producing durable copies, so that the message can be filed, stored, and referred to at will.)

4. The message deals with spatial orientation or with the location of points in space. (Show someone how to get from point A to point B with the help of a map. Now try to tell someone else the same thing using only spoken words. Which is easier?)

5. There is no urgency in the transmission of the message.

6. The available auditory channels are overloaded or are already saturated with messages.

7. The auditory environment is not suitable for the transmission of aural communications. (For example, visual signals are often more suitable for transmitting messages in such noisy places as the riveting section of a factory and in the immediate vicinity of jet aircraft.)

8. The operator's job allows him to stay in one spot. (In order to receive visual messages the recipient must have his eyes focused on the receiving unit or must be sufficiently close to it that he can see the message when it arrives.)

9. The machine or system output consists of many different kinds of information (e.g., engine temperature, cylinder pressure, RPM, speed) which must be displayed simultaneously, monitored, and acted upon from time to time.

AURAL MEANS OF COMMUNICATION

Aural forms of communication (telephone, telegraph, face-to-face communication, buzzers, warning signals, and so on) are generally more suitable when:

1. The message is simple and uncomplicated. (For example, the words "Okay" or "Roger" are very easily transmitted by means of auditory communication.)

2. The message to be transmitted is short.

3. Speed of transmission of the message is important. (If you want to signal somebody to "Jump!" an auditory message is probably the best way to do it. Auditory signals, in general, also have greater attention-getting value than visual ones.)

4. The message does not need to be referred to later.

5. The message deals with events in time and with a particular point in time. (For example, if you want to signal somebody exactly when he should launch a missile or start a race, an auditory communication system will enable you to pinpoint this time easily and with precision.)

6. Visual channels of communication are overloaded.

7. The environment is not suitable for the reception of visual messages. (For example, in the presence of excessive vibration, or in the absence of all illumination, auditory transmission systems may be the only ones feasible.)

8. The operator has to move around a lot. (We have already noted that our ears are always alert for messages,

which can be received from any direction. If the operator must continually move about in the work environment, an aural form of communication is more likely to get through to him.)

9. There is a chance that the operator may be subjected to anoxia (lack of oxygen due to high altitudes) or to the effects of positive acceleration. (The auditory sense is much more resistant than the eye to anoxia of the brain. An operator can hear messages when he may be temporarily blind because of the lack of oxygen.)

10. The problem is one of detecting a signal in the presence of concealing noise. (The ear is a very sensitive frequency analyzer. That is why you can hear, or single out for perception, the sound of a flute from the sound of an entire orchestra. If all the sound waves originating from the orchestra were put into a visual display, such as a cathode-ray tube, you would never be able to isolate the output of a single instrument. It is this ability of the ear to detect a particular signal in the presence of many other signals that makes the ear a very sensitive detector in systems such as sonar—the underwater exploration and location of objects such as submarines.)

This evaluation of the relative advantages and disadvantages of visual and aural communication systems makes it clear that there are many situations in which it is appropriate to use one, and many other situations in which it is appropriate to use the other. In any case, one should not try to make the eyes or ears do jobs for which they are not suited.

Vision as a Channel of Communication

Most of us grow up so impressed by the gadgets in our mechanized society that we often overlook the intricate mechanisms we have in our own bodies. Few of us appreciate, for example, what a marvelous transducer we have in the human eye. With this instrument, a normal human being can, under good conditions, see a wire $\frac{1}{16}$ inch in diameter at a distance of half a mile (15). It is so sensitive that when it is fully dark-adapted the average person can see the flare of a match 50 miles away on a clear, dark night. On the other hand, the eye can look momentarily at the sun at its zenith. The ratio of these two intensities is about 100,000,000,000,000:1! The average person, moreover, can discriminate several hundred thousand different colors. There is no single physical instrument that even begins to approach the flexibility and sensitivity of the human eye.

The sense of sight also renders remarkable psychological service as an information channel. Man's eyes are his major source of contact with his environment. They furnish him with his primary means of knowing things and of finding his way about in life. Think of the wealth of information you have gained from the books, magazines, and newspapers you have read so far in your life. It is not surprising that when man becomes a functioning part of a man-machine system, his effectiveness is often determined entirely by the acuity and efficiency with which he can use his eyes. Take radar, for example. Radar has been called "the eyes that guard our skies." But radar doesn't *see*. It's a man who sees. And if the human operator cannot see information on a radar scope because of poorly designed equipment or poor lighting, the radar is useless and the system fails.

Visual problems are numerous and important in man-machine systems: What is the best kind of dial to use? How should dials be designed? What size and design of lettering should be used on highway signs? What colors of light are best for signaling at night? How far away can an astronaut see another space capsule in outer space? These are only a few of the questions about vision which a human factors engineer might be asked to answer. In this chapter we shall be able to deal with only a small portion of the information available about vision and visual displays. For more detailed information, consult any of the several books in the References (6, 23, 25).

Some General Principles of Visual Display

There is more to choosing or designing a good visual display than just making it visible. First of all, a good display presents information in a form that can be easily understood and interpreted by the people who have to use it. Further, a good display presents information in a form that can easily be converted into correct decisions and appropriate actions. These general requirements mean that a visual display cannot be designed as an isolated item. It has to be designed for a particular environment and with a particular system in mind. Some of the general conditions the designer must always keep in mind are the following:

1. *Viewing distance.* The distance at which a display is to be used is important in determining the size of its details, their spacing and arrangement, and sometimes their color and illumination. Some displays, like books, tables, and graphs, are designed to be read at distances no greater than about 16 inches. Other displays, such as dials and gauges, are often intended to be used in conjunction with controls of some sort and so should be designed to be read at no more than arm's length (about 28 inches). Still other displays, like highway signs, wall clocks, and airport beacons, are designed to be seen at distances ranging from a few yards to several miles.

2. *Illumination.* Some visual displays (for example, cathode-ray tubes and warning lights) have built-in sources of illumination; others (for example, road markings and labels) depend on external sources. Some have to be read in poor illumination; others may be well lit. Sometimes the source of illumination is strongly colored and distorts the natural colors of objects; at other times the illumination approximates that of natural daylight. All of these conditions are factors that influence the choice of kind, size, and color of the visual display.

3. *Angle of view.* In general, visual displays are best read when they are in (perpendicular to) the direct line of sight. However, since many displays (see, for example, Fig. 2–5) are large consoles occupying a considerable area, not all parts of the display can be viewed perpendicularly from any single vantage point. In addition, when several operators must use the same display, it is impossible for all of them to view the display perpendicularly. In such circumstances, the designer must take special precautions to avoid excessive parallax in or obscuring some parts of the display.

4. *The total ensemble of displays.* Visual displays such as dials, lights, and indicators seldom appear in isolation. Instead, they often appear on consoles along with numerous other displays. In such circumstances the designer must try to ensure (a) that the information is presented *consistently* on the various displays (this rule is violated, for example, in the kilowatt-hour meters shown in Fig. 1–3), and (b) that the operator can easily and correctly identify a particular display when he wants to.

5. *Compatibility with associated controls.* When displays have to be used in conjunction with controls of some sort, and they often

are, the kind of display which is most appropriate is influenced by the kind of control action the operator has to make. (We shall see examples of this interaction in the next section.) The goal of the human engineer is to design and place a display and its control so that an operator, with little or no training, can find them readily, extract the information he needs, and make the correct kind of control movement with a minimum of time and error.

6. *General environmental conditions.* Man-machine systems do not operate in isolation; they operate in environments of various kinds. Vibration, acceleration (high g forces), anoxia (lack of oxygen), and other conditions have serious affects on man's ability to see. When displays are to be used under such adverse conditions, they must be designed accordingly.

7. *The operator population.* Since people differ markedly from one another, displays must be designed for the kinds of people who will use them. For example, displays used by elderly people with presbyopia, by color-blind people, or by the general population must be designed quite differently from those used exclusively by carefully selected, healthy, young men. In this connection, it is important to consider not only the visual capacities of the users, but their intellectual capacities as well. For example, people differ in span of apprehension (the number of digits or letters they can take in at a glance), speed of perception, and general intelligence. As a general rule, all these variables change markedly with age. This means, for example, that displays used by the very young or the very old should not contain as much information or be as complicated as those used only by men and women in their twenties.

Mechanical Indicators

There are many ways in which machines can present information to their human operators—lights, cathode-ray tubes, printed pages of data, and dials being a few of them. In this section we shall consider three common kinds of dials and indicators and look at a few of the important human-engineering principles that should determine their selection and design.

Functions of Mechanical Indicators

A visual indicator should be selected on the basis of its use— not its engineering use—although that is an important and relevant consideration, to be sure—but its use in giving the human operator the kind of information he needs in the way that he can best use it. Generally, mechanical indicators serve in one of the four functions discussed below.

QUANTITATIVE READING

One purpose of indicators is to provide exact numerical readings. You use a clock to find out the time, and, if you are rushing to make a plane connection, you want to know the time exactly. You use a thermometer to find out the exact temperature of the room you are in, the roast you have in your oven, or the photographic developer you use in your basement darkroom. Compasses, speedometers, kilowatt-hour meters, tachometers, and thousands of other indicators are designed to provide precise quantitative readings.

CHECK READING

Not all dials and indicators are used for getting exact information. Let's take a simple case. Do you need to know the *exact* running temperature of the engine in your automobile? Do you care whether it's 160°, 161°, or even 183°? Most people don't care, and there is no reason to tell them. But what do they need to know? Mostly, they need to know whether the engine temperature is *about* right. The safe operating range of the engine is so broad that variations of a couple of degrees more or less are nothing to get excited about. All that most drivers want to know is whether the engine temperature is within its normal operating range. That is a simple check reading—a GO, NO-GO, or OK, NOT-OK type of indication.

An engine thermometer could give the driver a little more information as well. Should he develop a leak in the radiator of his car, it is very helpful to see not only that the temperature is at the high end of the normal operating range but that the reading is increasing with time. This kind of modified check reading tells the alert driver that he had better stop and check the water level in his radiator.

Perhaps the most important thing to notice about either kind of check reading is that there is often no necessity for putting any numbers on the instrument. For many purposes the dial on the right in Figure 3–1 is far superior to that on the left. In simple check readings a dial may not be necessary at all. A warning light is often all that is needed.

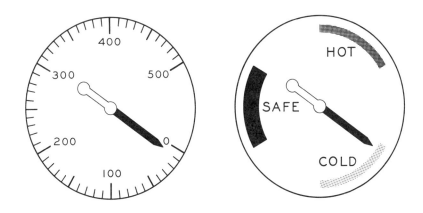

FIGURE 3–1. *For check-reading purposes, dials such as those on the right are less complex and usually easier to interpret than those on the left.*

SETTING

The two uses of indicators discussed above are essentially concerned with the extraction of information from machines. Sometimes, however, a visual indicator is linked to a control so that the operator can tell exactly what information he is putting into a machine. When you turn the alarm knob on your clock, you want some *feedback* so that you can be sure you have turned the knob the correct amount to wake you at seven o'clock in the morning. When you set the thermostat for your furnace, you need some sort of indication to tell you exactly what instructions you have given the system. These are homely and familiar examples of a type you can find repeated hundreds of ways in machine shops, factories, airplanes, and ships. All of them illustrate the use of visual indicators for setting information into machines.

TRACKING

When the captain of a ship tells the helmsman to turn the ship from bearing 120° to 130°, the helmsman turns a wheel. This activates the rudder and gradually brings the ship around to the desired heading. As the ship turns, a dial on the compass turns too, the numbers and markers on the compass floating past a "lubberline," or index marker. When the setting of 130° appears under the index marker, the ship is on its correct course.

Gusts of wind, waves, and ocean currents tend to force the ship off its course from time to time. The task of the helmsman is to make the proper corrective movements with his wheel so that the number 130° is brought back under the index marker whenever it drifts off. In a large ship, deviations occur relatively slowly and infrequently. In a small ship, or aircraft, they may happen rapidly and often. However fast the action, the task is basically a tracking task. It occurs not only in the examples mentioned above, but in driving an automobile and in a great variety of special military machines. Perhaps you can imagine what some of them are.

Types of Indicators and Their Uses

There is always some danger in trying to summarize complex recommendations in a simple way. One difficulty arises because instruments are occasionally used for several purposes. In such cases, it is usually necessary to make a careful analysis of the total job and to decide which of the several functions is the most important. Then, too, there are sometimes special considerations that override any general rule one could make. If we keep these precautions in mind, Figure 3–2 can be taken as a useful summary of the relative advantages and disadvantages of three main types of indicators, according to their uses. A + means that the indicator is good for that function, a o means that it is only fair or questionable, and a — means that you should generally avoid using that indicator for the purpose shown.

COUNTERS AND MOVING POINTERS

If the sole purpose of an indicator is to provide exact numerical information, a *counter* is the best way to do it. As just one example, compare the kilowatt-hour meter in Figure 3–3 with the two you saw in Figure 1–3. You hardly need any research to tell you which is the easiest and fastest to read.

For check reading, the *moving-pointer* type of instrument is the best of the three. The orientation of the pointer is easy to see, and it is a simple and useful cue to the approximate setting of the indicator. In fact, if you indicate the safe or normal operating range with a stripe on the edge of the dial, the operator need not read any numbers at all (see Fig. 3–1). He merely has to see whether the needle is pointing to the stripe. If it is, everything is OK. If it is not, something needs adjusting or attention. Note also that the position and movements of the needle provide some of the additional information an operator occasionally needs for check reading, such as the *direction* of deviation and changes with *time*. Neither the moving-scale indicator nor the counter is very good for check reading, because it is difficult to judge the direction and amount of the deviation without first reading the numbers. This procedure involves at least two steps: (a) the operator must first read the indicator—that is, extract a number; and then (b) decide what the number means. Although you could paint a section to show normal operating ranges on both these indicators, telling the direction in which a deviation occurs is somewhat more difficult.

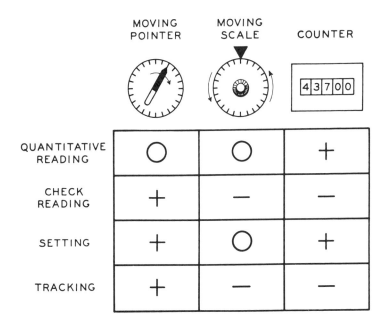

FIGURE 3–2. *Recommended uses for three basic types of indicators.*

For setting information into a machine, either a moving-pointer dial or a counter is good. The former is good because changes in the position of the pointer help the operator make his setting. He can see the pointer move and judge how far he has to move it. In addition, it is easy to get a simple and direct relationship between the direction of movement of the pointer and the direction of movement of the control which activates it. On the other hand, settings can generally be monitored more accurately with a counter than with a moving-pointer instrument. To offset this, however, there is the disadvantage that a counter cannot be read when settings are changing rapidly. In addition, it is somewhat harder to provide an unambiguous relationship

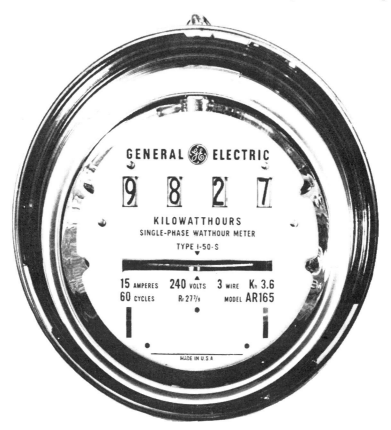

FIGURE 3–3. *This kilowatt-hour meter illustrates one of the principles summarized in Figure 3–2. For quantitative readings, it is far superior to the two dials in Figure 1–3.*

between movements of a control and the settings on a counter. If a knob is linked to a counter, you may not always be sure which way to turn the knob to increase or decrease the setting. This kind of ambiguity can be avoided with the moving-pointer instrument.

The moving-pointer instrument is best for tracking because movements of the pointer are easy to monitor and control. It is, moreover, simple to get easily interpreted relationships between the movements of the pointer and its related control.

THE MOVING-SCALE INDICATOR

You will notice from Figure 3–2 that the *moving-scale* indicator does not show up very well at all. Thereby hangs an interesting psychological tale. The trouble with this indicator is that there is no way to design it without violating one of three important principles. These three rules are:

1. The scale and the knob (crank, or wheel) that controls it should rotate in the same direction. (When you turn the knob clockwise, the scale should rotate clockwise. When you turn the knob counterclockwise, the scale should move counterclockwise.)

2. A clockwise rotation of the knob should increase the settings on the scale; a counterclockwise rotation should decrease settings.

3. The numbers on the scale should increase in a clockwise direction around the scale. Scales are read with less confusion when numbers progress in this way.

With these three rules in front of us, we can see what's wrong with the moving-scale indicator. There is no way to design an indicator of this type so that all three rules are satisfied at the same time. As an exercise, draw up at least three variants of this kind of indicator. Suppose you were to mark "Normal," "Hot," and "Cold" zones around the periphery of these scales (as was done in Fig. 3–1). What ambiguities or problems of interpretation would still remain?

Despite the difficulties noted above, you can find indicators of this type on many different kinds of equipment. The drawing in Figure 3–4 is a schematic illustration of a moving-scale indicator on an electric room heater. The black triangular figure at the top is a fixed index marker. To turn the knob, you grasp the raised flange in the center with your fingers. But which way do you turn it to increase the heat? There is an arrow on the left side of the dial pointing to the word *HI*. Perhaps this means that you should turn the knob in the direction of that arrow—that is, counterclockwise—to increase the heat. On the other hand, perhaps you are supposed to turn the knob so that the word *HI* is brought more nearly under the index marker. But that would be a clockwise rotation of the knob. Perhaps you can see why people get perplexed by this device. How can this sort of ambiguity be eliminated? The answer, according to the recommendations given in Figure 3–2, is to convert the display into a moving-pointer display (Fig. 3–5). I think you will agree that there is no difficulty in interpreting this one.

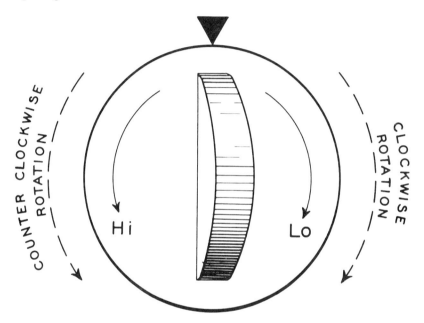

FIGURE 3–4.   *Schematic illustration of the heat control on an electric room heater.*

In the case of an electric heater, no very great harm is done if you turn the heat down when you really meant to turn it up. However, I have seen this same kind of indicator on a very expensive jet aircraft trainer. An engineer for the company that designed the trainer confessed that some pilots went one way, others the opposite way. In a jet aircraft, such ambiguity is no longer a trivial matter.

For another example of the confusion caused by moving-scale indicators, look at the micrometer in Figure 3–6. This one is graduated in inches; but even with that information, can you read the setting?

If you have had no prior experience with instruments of this sort, the chances are that you will be thoroughly confused.

Note first that the numerals o, 1, 2, 3, etc., on the frame of the micrometer represent tenths of inches. Second, notice that there are four marked divisions between the numbers. They mean that each marked interval corresponds to o.1 ÷ 4, or o.025 inch. In addition, the thimble (the section at the end of the micrometer) makes one

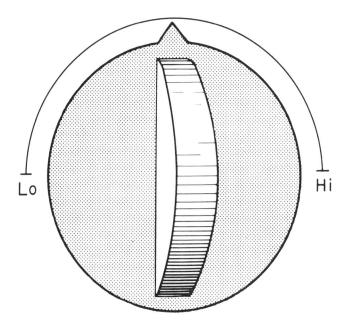

FIGURE 3–5. *This heater control eliminates the ambiguities found in the one illustrated in Figure 3–4.*

complete revolution per marked interval on the frame, and there are twenty-five small marked intervals around the circumference of the thimble. Hence, each of the latter corresponds to o.025 ÷ 25, or o.001 inch. Now, with this information, can you read the setting on the micrometer?

If we return to the recommendations given in Figure 3–2, we see that a much better way of portraying quantitative information of this kind is to use a direct-reading counter. Figure 3–7 shows a micrometer

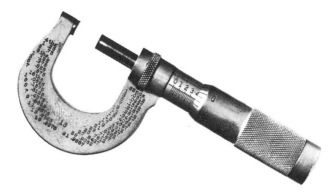

FIGURE 3–6.   *A micrometer of conventional design.*

designed in this way. The improvement is so obvious that no further words of explanation are needed. (See also Chapanis, 5.)

FIGURE 3–7.   *A micrometer designed for easy readability.*

The Design of Dials and Scales

If a human factors engineer decides that a moving-pointer indicator is appropriate for his purpose, the next thing he needs to consider is: How should the indicator be designed? This section discusses a few principles of dial and scale design.

Some useful general rules for the design of dials and scales are these:

1. A scale should be designed so that an operator can read information as accurately as he needs, but no more accurately.

2. A scale should be the simplest that will meet the operator's needs; that is, it should not provide more information than is necessary.

3. The scale should provide information in an immediately usable form. The operator should not have to make mental conversions from indicated values to the values he really needs.

4. Scales that are to be read quantitatively should be designed so that the operator does not need to interpolate between marks. Insofar as possible, scales should be designed to be read to the nearest graduation mark.

NUMBERING SYSTEMS AND GRADUATION MARKS

A considerable amount of research has been done on the numbering systems used on scales and on how these systems affect the speed and accuracy of reading scales. (See pp. 21–23 for an illustration of one of these studies.) Figure 3–8 summarizes the general recommendations that have come out of this research. The left-hand column of this figure shows the *graduation-interval value* (the value of the smallest division on the scale). Notice that only three numerals are recommended—1, 2, and 5, or decimal multiples of these digits. No other values are acceptable, because people cannot as readily interpret or use scales that are graduated in other ways. The *numbered-interval values* are the values between any two major graduation marks—the marks to which numerals are attached. Here again the only recommended numerals are 1, 2, and 5, or decimal multiples of them. Fortunately, since the basic numerical values can be multiplied or divided by factors of ten or a hundred without appreciably affecting the speed or accuracy with which scales can be read, a scale that is numbered 0, 10, 20, 30, etc., or 0, 100, 200, 300, etc., is just about as easy to read as one that is numbered 0, 1, 2, 3, etc.

The extreme right column of Figure 3–8 shows recommendations about the graduation marks to be used on scales. There are three

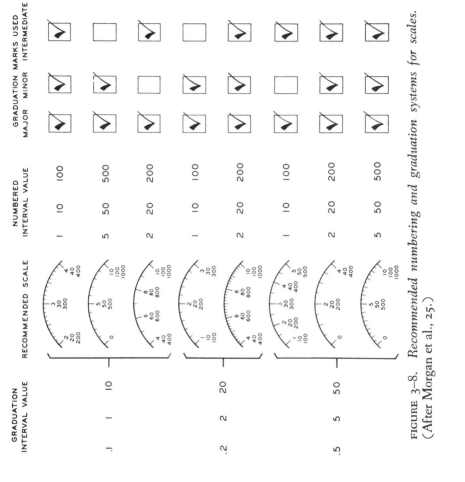

FIGURE 3–8. *Recommended numbering and graduation systems for scales.* (After Morgan et al., 25.)

kinds of graduation marks: major, minor, and intermediate. Some scales should use all three types of markings; some should use only the major and minor marks; some should use the major and intermediate marks. The check marks show which combinations of marks should be used for each kind of scale.

With the samples of recommended scales shown in Figure 3–8, it should be possible to design a scale to meet almost any requirement. The scale at the top of the column, however, is generally superior to the others, and so should be preferred whenever possible.

THE DIMENSIONS OF GRADUATION MARKS

It is difficult to give any single set of recommendations for the design of scale markings because of the many factors involved: for instance, the general level of illumination, reading distance, and the number of markings. The minimum dimensions shown in Figure 3–9 are recommended for scales which are to be read under dim il-

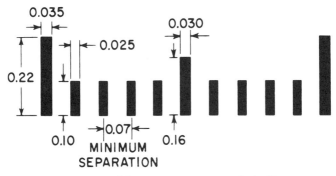

FIGURE 3–9. *Minimum recommended dimensions for markings on scales that will be read under dim illuminations.* (After Morgan et al., 25.)

lumination from a distance of 28 inches. The dimensions in the figure are useful as models for relative sizes, which may be increased or decreased proportionately for other reading distances.

Scales that are to be read under normal illumination should have the same relative proportions as are shown in Figure 3–9, but the graduation marks may be spaced as closely as 0.035 inch. In any case, the minimum distance between major graduation marks should not be less than 0.5 inch, and the heights of the major, intermediate, and minor marks should not be less than 0.22, 0.16, and 0.09 inch, respectively.

AN APPLICATION OF THESE DIAL-DESIGN PRINCIPLES

Examples of poor dial design are relatively easy to find; Figure 3–10 is only one of many. This is a particularly interesting one, how-

FIGURE 3–10. *On the left is a pneumatic-indicator dial as originally manufactured; on the right, the same dial after redesign.*

ever, because it is a "before-and-after" illustration. The dial on the left had been manufactured at the Bristol Company, the manufacturer of a wide variety of meters and recording instruments. The dial on the right is the same one after redesign. In addition to being more legible, the dial on the right uses a much more satisfactory numbering system.

The experience of this company is instructive. Purchasers of one of their instruments frequently misread critical settings and thought the instrument was out of calibration. After the dial had been redesigned, these errors were greatly reduced and customer complaints dropped markedly. In a report to his management, J. G. Fleming stated, ". . . we are just amazed at the consequence of simply changing scale markings." Other examples of "before-and-after" designs can be found in Fleming's article (12).

Illumination

Our eyes need light to see. This simple and self-evident fact means that visual displays are effective only if they are provided with enough illumination of the right kind. The solution to most problems of illumination, however, is not simply to flood the work environment with large quantities of light. In many man-machine systems, conflicting visual requirements greatly limit the amount of light that may be used. For example, the pilot of a commercial airliner or the captain of a ship must have dial markings and visual displays bright enough to see correctly. On the other hand, these men may have to scan the outside world at night, and to do so effectively, their eyes must be dark adapted. This is a situation in which some sort of compromise must be reached.

Problems of illumination can be grouped under three general headings: (a) general workplace illumination, (b) illumination for radar rooms, and (c) indicator and panel lighting. We shall have something to say about each of these, but first we need to define some illumination terms and the units in which they are measured.

The Nature of the Visual Stimulus

We see things either because they emit radiant energy or because radiant energy is reflected from them. Common sources of radiant energy are the sun, moon, electric lights, and flames of various sorts. Although there is no complete agreement among theoretical physicists about the nature of radiant energy, it is conventional to talk about it as though it traveled in a wave form. In such terms, one fundamental dimension of radiant energy is its *wavelength,* the distance from pulse to pulse of a vibration. The complete spectrum of radiant energy covers an enormous range—from wavelengths that are only ten-trillionths of an inch in length (cosmic rays) to those that are many miles in length (electric circuits). Between these extremes are sections, or bands, of the spectrum that have been assigned distinctive names— X rays, ultraviolet rays, the visible spectrum, infrared rays, radar waves, and radio waves (FM, television, shortwave, and broadcast bands). These designations are more or less arbitrary, because, as far as we can tell, the radiations are fundamentally the same. They differ only in wavelength.

LIGHT WAVES

Radiant energy is a physical concept that has nothing to do with seeing. In fact, most radiant energy is invisible to the normal eye. Near the middle of the electromagnetic spectrum, however, is a small section that we can see. This section is called the *visible spectrum* and it consists of those waves which are roughly from 16 to 32 millionths of an inch in length. When a beam of white light is dispersed by a prism into its component wavelengths, the visible spectrum appears as a variegated display of vivid colors. With deep violet at the short-wavelength end of the spectrum, the colors shade imperceptibly into bluish-purple, blue, blue-green, green, yellow-green, yellow, orange, and deep red at the long-wavelength end.

Practically never, however, does an ordinary person see the colors produced by isolated wavelengths of radiation. The light coming from most objects is a mixture of a large number of wavelengths, and it is the particular combination of these wavelengths and the relative amounts of energy in them that gives an object its characteristic color. If the distribution of wavelengths in a ray of light is known, its color can be specified exactly. The reverse, however, is not true. A given color can be produced by any of an infinite number of wavelength combinations. Colors seen when the eye is stimulated by a single wavelength, or by a small band of adjacent wavelengths, are usually strongly *chromatic*; that is, strongly colored. The colors seen when the eye is stimulated by broad-band stimuli—that is, those containing a large number of different wavelengths—are usually much less strongly chromatic and more nearly white in appearance.

Light waves are commonly measured in millimicrons (mμ) or angstrom units (A). Although we shall use only the former measure in this book, this equation shows how the two are related to each other and to a more familiar unit of length:

$$1 \text{ m}\mu = 10 \, A = 10^{-9} \text{ meters.}$$

INTENSITY OF LIGHT SOURCE

When we speak of an amount of light, we could be referring to any of three different kinds of measures: (1) the total amount of light coming from a luminous object, such as an electric light bulb; (2) the amount of light falling on an object, such as a desk; or (3) the amount of light coming from an object that reflects light, such as a piece of paper on a desk.

The *intensity* of small sources of light is expressed in terms of the *candela* (abbreviated cd), or *new candle,* an arbitrarily defined photometric unit standardized by the national laboratories of most major countries. A standard candela is maintained at the National Bureau of Standards in Washington, for example; if you want to measure the intensity of an unknown light source, you can compare it with that standard candela—or with other working standards that have been calibrated at the National Bureau of Standards. If your unknown light source is twice as bright as the standard, it has an intensity of 2 cd. If it is half as intense as the standard, it has an intensity of ½ cd.

ILLUMINATION

Illumination (or *illuminance,* as it is more properly termed by scientists) is a measure of the total quantity of light falling onto a surface. A 1-candela source delivers 1 *foot-candle* (abbreviated ft-c) of illumination on a surface when the surface is 1 foot away from the source. An 8-cd source gives twice as much illumination as a 4-cd source and four times as much illumination as a 2-cd source, because the illumination falling on a surface is directly proportional to the intensity of the light source.

Another characteristic of illumination is that a surface twice as far away from a light receives one-quarter as much illumination and a surface three times as far away gets one-ninth as much illumination. In short, the illumination on a surface is inversely proportional to the square of the distance between the surface and the light. Both of these generalizations are combined in the following equation:

$$E = \frac{I}{d^2}$$

where E = the illuminance in foot-candles,

I = the intensity of the source in candelas, and

d = the distance between the source and the illuminated surface in feet.

There are a number of other measures of illuminance you will run across from time to time. Some of these are the *mile-candle, centimeter-candle* (or *phot*), and *meter-candle* (or *lux*). They are obtained from the equation above simply by changing the unit in which d, the distance between the source and the surface, is measured. The following equation shows how these measures are related:

1 ft-c = 2.79 × 10⁷ mile-c = 1.08 × 10⁻³ phot = 10.8 lux.

LUMINANCE

The third kind of measure often used in practical work is the amount of light coming from objects that reflect light. In ordinary speech, we refer to this as the *brightness* of a surface. The term *brightness* is much too loose for exact work, however, because we also speak of the brightness of the beacon in a lighthouse (when we really mean its intensity), the brightness of the sunlight falling on the dashboard of an automobile (when we really mean its illuminance), or the brightness of an afterimage (when the "light" is generated entirely within the eye). For these reasons, the expert uses the exact term *luminance* to refer specifically to the amount of light reflected from an object.

Even though a uniform distribution of light falls on the top of a desk, the amount of light that comes back from different objects on the desk will vary greatly. The amount of light reflected from a piece of dark paper will be small; the amount of light coming back from the white page of a book will be considerably greater. In other words, the two surfaces differ in luminance.

A common unit of luminance is the *apparent foot-candle* (abbreviated app ft-c), or its exact equivalent, the *foot-lambert* (abbreviated ft-L). If you had a perfectly reflecting surface—a surface that reflected all the light that fell on it—and put 1 foot-candle of illuminance on it, that surface would have a luminance of 1 apparent foot-candle. If you have a surface that reflects 90 per cent of the light that falls on it— and this is about as good as one can get with white paper—and put 1 foot-candle of illuminance on it, it will have a luminance of 0.9 apparent foot-candles. In short, to measure the luminance of a surface in apparent foot-candles, multiply the illuminance on the surface (in foot-candles) by the overall reflectance of the surface.

There are many different measures of luminance, depending on how you measure illuminance and the units in which you measure distances or lengths. Three of the most common ones are the apparent foot-candle, the *millilambert* (mL), and the *candle per square centimeter* (c/cm²). The following equation shows how these are related to each other:

$$1 \text{ app ft-c} = 1.08 \text{ mL} = 3.43 \times 10^{-4} \text{ c/cm}^2.$$

General Workplace Illumination

Under this heading are included all those systems used for providing light in such relatively uncomplicated environments as the home, office, school, and factory. Although these are usually straightforward situations, the design and specification of an appropriate lighting system must consider such things as:

a. The nature of the visual tasks that will be performed.

b. The quantity of light that must be provided.

c. The uniformity of the lighting.

d. Glare and reflections from light sources and work areas.

e. The quality and color of the illuminants and the work areas.

Levels and types of illumination that are satisfactory for most general purposes are summarized in Table 3–1.

ARTIFICIAL LIGHTING SYSTEMS

Artificial lighting systems for general workplace illumination are of three principal kinds: (a) direct lighting, (b) indirect lighting, and (c) diffuse lighting. Direct lighting is the most efficient way of getting light from a lighting unit to a work area, because as much as 90 per cent or more of the light from such a unit may be directed downward. Unfortunately, direct-lighting systems often produce annoying and distracting brightness contrasts, shadows, and glare. They are nonetheless particularly appropriate for floodlighting and for local illumination of important work areas.

Indirect lighting provides a more uniform distribution of light, without deep shadows and glare, by directing light toward the ceiling and walls, from which it is reflected round the room. Systems of this type, however, are relatively inefficient; and, if the reflectances of the ceiling, walls, and floor are not properly matched, they may make the ceiling a bright and annoying source of glare.

Diffuse lighting scatters light more or less evenly in all directions. It is usually more efficient than indirect lighting, but somewhat less efficient than direct lighting. Excessive glare and shadows can be virtually eliminated by diffuse-lighting systems made of fluorescent tubes with baffles. Newer, highly effective indirect systems make use of fluorescent tubes above translucent panels set into the ceiling of a room.

GLARE

Dazzle or glare produced by light sources of relatively high intensity are especially harmful to effective vision. Glare may be caused by light sources directly in the field of view, or by bright surfaces that reflect light into the eyes (*specular* glare). However produced, glare of any kind usually decreases visual acuity markedly and often produces

TABLE 3-1. *Levels of illumination and types of illumination recommended for various task conditions.* (From Morgan et al., 25.)

TASK CONDITION	TYPE OF TASK OR AREA	ILLUMINATION LEVEL (ft-c)	TYPE OF ILLUMINATION
Small detail, low brightness contrast, prolonged periods, high speed, extreme accuracy	Sewing, inspecting dark materials, etc.	100	General plus supplementary (e.g., desk lamp)
Small detail, fair contrast, speed not essential	Machining, detail drafting, watch repairing, inspecting medium materials, etc.	50–100	General plus supplementary
Normal detail, prolonged periods	Reading, parts assembly, general office and laboratory work	20–50	General (e.g., overhead ceiling fixture)
Normal detail, no prolonged periods	Washrooms, power plants, waiting rooms, kitchens	10–20	General (e.g., random natural or artificial light)
Good contrast, fairly large objects	Recreational facilities	5–10	General
Large objects	Restaurants, stairways, bulk-supply warehouses	2–5	General

physical effects such as watering of the eyes, excessive blinking, and headaches.

Direct glare can be controlled by using indirect lighting, by using shields, hoods, and visors to keep direct light out of the operator's eyes, or by using several low-intensity sources rather than a single high-intensity source. Specular glare can be effectively controlled by using diffuse light and dull, mat surfaces rather than polished ones, or by arranging light sources so that viewing angles do not coincide with the angles of reflectance from the light sources to work areas.

COLOR

The normal eye has an appreciable amount of chromatic aberration, which tends to blur the edges of images formed on the retina. Theoretically, therefore, one might expect that visual acuity should be better under highly chromatic illumination than under general, broad-band illumination. Actual experimental data show, however, that no chromatic illumination is better than natural daylight. Artificial illuminants that approximate natural daylight or that emit light throughout the entire visual spectrum, such as tungsten and fluorescent lamps, are usually far better than strongly chromatic illuminants. As a general rule, colored filters should not be used over most lamps for ordinary purposes of illumination. A colored filter always reduces the total quantity of light emitted from a lamp, and this loss of light usually does more to reduce the ability of the eye to see than the color does to increase it.

Purple lights are composed of mixtures of wavelengths from opposite ends of the visual spectrum—that is, of red light from the long-wavelength end, and blue light from the short-wavelength end. The normal eye is completely unable to focus clearly on objects illuminated with lights of this character. Such lights are particularly appropriate, therefore, as night lights in bedrooms and sleeping cars, because they provide a general, low level of illumination without emphasizing or highlighting details in the environment.

Special care has to be taken in the specification of illuminants for work environments where precise color matching is required, as, for example, in the government grading of hay, butter, and cotton, or in the commercial grading of paper, tiles, and cartons for thousands of household products. Fluorescent lamps generally produce light through the excitation of phosphorescent chemicals on the inside of the tube. These chemicals are in turn triggered by the excitation of mercury or other inert gases in the tube when an electric current is passed through them. Such gases do not emit continuously throughout the spectrum; rather, they emit at discrete wavelengths. Mercury vapor, for example, has five strong emission lines: two in the blue, two in the yellow-green, and one in the deep-red end of the spectrum. Since the eye is an integrator, it responds to these emission lines with a single color sensation not much different from daylight. When light of this kind is reflected from colored surfaces, however, serious color distortions may occur. For example, fresh meats, which appear bright red in soft white light, may look spoiled in a refrigerator case illuminated with daylight fluorescent light. Accessories that appear to be perfectly matched to clothing under artificial light may clash under daylight. For most purposes in which precise discriminations have to be made, lamps should be selected or designed to approximate C.I.E. Illuminant C (18), a kind of standard illuminant that comes close to matching natural daylight.

Illumination for Radar Rooms

Radar was originally designed for military purposes, but it has become an important and standard component in many man-machine systems—for civilian air-traffic-control systems, in sea- and air-navigation systems, and in automobile-traffic-surveillance systems. In designing illumination for radar rooms, three conflicting requirements must be met:

1. The lighting system should provide enough general or ambient illumination for radar operators to walk around, for maintenance men to attend to their duties, and so on.

2. Ambient illumination should not be allowed to reach the face of the scope because, if it should, there will be a reduction in the target-to-background brightness contrast and hence a reduction in the visibility of targets.

3. Indirect reflections from the face of the scope should not be allowed to reach the operator's eyes.

Four ingenious lighting systems have been designed to cope with this situation: a cross-polarization system, a broad-band-blue system, a sodium-minus-yellow system, and a mercury-minus-red system. All

four of these lighting systems have much in common; so we shall illustrate the general principles they utilize by describing one of them
in detail.

In the *broad-band-blue system,* general room illumination is provided by lamps that emit radiation throughout the entire visible spectrum (for example, fluorescent or tungsten lamps). The lamps are covered with blue filters that transmit only radiation shorter than, say,
540 mµ. This means, therefore, that the room is flooded with blue light
of sufficient intensity for people to carry out routine duties.

The second part of the system consists of another set of filters,
which transmit radiation only above 540 mµ. These filters are placed
over the radar scopes. Since the wavelengths passed by the blue filters
of the room lamps are absorbed by these second filters, none of the
ambient light reaches the face of the scope.

The third part of the system consists of goggles, which the radar
operators wear. These goggles contain filters that exactly match the
filters on the radar scopes, allowing the radar operator to see the scope.
However, since the filters in the goggles are incompatible with the
filters over the room lights, the operator cannot see the general room
illumination, either directly or indirectly, when it is reflected from objects around the room.

The broad-band-blue system and the other three lighting systems
satisfy the three requirements stated earlier: (a) they distribute enough
light around the room so that people can move about; (b) they do not
reduce the target-to-background contrasts on the scope; and (c) they
eliminate specular reflections. Unfortunately, these advantages come at
a price. In the cross-polarization system, the light fixtures and filters
have to be positioned with extreme care, so that the light will be
properly polarized at all critical places in the room. In addition, polariz-
ing filters do not transmit as much light as do some of the other filters
available in the other three systems. The principal disadvantages of the
latter—the broad-band-blue, the sodium-minus-yellow, and the mercury-minus-red systems—are (a) that colors used for coding purposes
are likely to be seriously distorted in the highly chromatic illumination,
(b) that some people tend to be emotionally affected by strongly
chromatic illuminants, and (c) that these systems will not work with
certain types of phosphors on cathode-ray tubes. Because the broad-
band-blue system makes use of much more of the visible spectrum
than do either the sodium-minus-yellow or the mercury-minus-red sys-

tems, illumination in the former is not as strongly colored as in the other two. Experience over the past ten years in numerous centers suggests that, everything considered, the broad-band-blue is the best of the four.

Indicator and Panel Lighting

In trying to provide suitable lighting for indicators and instrument panels, one often has to face the conflicting requirements mentioned at the beginning of this section: Dials and other visual displays must have enough illumination so that they can be seen well, but not so much illumination that they affect the operator's ability to see outside his work area at night. Fortunately, it is possible to exploit an unusual property of the human eye in such situations.

RED LIGHT FOR DARK ADAPTATION

The human eye contains two basic types of photosensitive nerve endings in the retina: the *rods* and *cones*. The cones function primarily under conditions of daylight illumination and the rods function under extremely dark conditions (roughly, below the level of full moonlight). Both require an appreciable period of time to reach maximum sensitivity after they have been exposed to bright lights. The rods especially are slow to adapt; depending on the intensity, color, and duration of the light, the rods may require as long as thirty minutes to reach full sensitivity after having been exposed to a bright light. The rods and cones are not equally sensitive to all parts of the visible spectrum. The cones are more sensitive to long wavelengths (the red end) whereas the rods are more sensitive to the short wavelengths (the blue end) of the spectrum. This differential sensitivity means that when we use red light to allow the cones to see, the rods at the same time are, in a manner of speaking, sitting in darkness.

The use of red illumination to preserve the dark adaptation of the rods has many practical applications in addition to illuminating indicators and panels. X-ray technicians, for example, may find it necessary to come out of a darkroom from time to time to pick up exposed film, or for other purposes. To preserve their dark adaptation so that they can see when they return to the darkroom, they will often slip on a pair of red goggles just before they leave the darkroom. When they return to the darkroom, they remove the goggles and find that their dark-adapted rods are virtually at full sensitivity. As another example, ready

TABLE 3–2. *Recommendations for indicator, panel, and chart lighting.* (From Morgan et al., 25.)

CONDITION OF USE	LIGHTING TECHNIQUE	RECOMMENDATIONS LUMINANCE OF MARKINGS (ft-L)	BRIGHTNESS ADJUSTMENT
Indicator reading, dark adaptation necessary	Red flood, indirect, or both, with operator choice	0.02–0.1	Continuous throughout range
Indicator reading, dark adaptation not necessary but desirable	Red or low-color-temperature white flood, indirect, or both, with operator choice	0.02–1.0	Continuous throughout range
Indicator reading, dark adaptation not necessary	White flood	1–20	Fixed or continuous
Panel monitoring, dark adaptation necessary	Red edge lighting, red or white flood, or both, with operator choice	0.02–1.0	Continuous throughout range
Panel monitoring, dark adaptation not necessary	White flood	10–20	Fixed or continuous
Indicator reading or panel monitoring with possible exposure to bright flashes	White flood	10–20	Fixed
Indicator reading or panel monitoring at very high altitude and restricted daylight	White flood	10–20	Fixed
Chart reading, dark adaptation necessary	Red or white flood, with operator choice	0.1–1.0 (on white portions of chart)	Continuous throughout range
Chart reading, dark adaptation not necessary	White flood	5–20	Fixed or continuous

rooms aboard aircraft carriers or in shore-based installations are usually equipped with red illumination so that pilots will be prepared to take off on night-flying missions with their eyes adjusted to darkness.

RECOMMENDATIONS FOR INDICATOR LIGHTING

Table 3-2 summarizes recommendations about lighting systems for dials, indicators, instrument panels, and charts according to the conditions under which they will be used. You will notice that red light is recommended whenever dark adaptation is critical.

Summary

In this chapter we have been introduced to the problems of machine displays—to ways in which our machine environment communicates information to us. The chapter opened with some general considerations regarding the choice between visual and auditory means of communication. It then summarized some general principles of visual display and concentrated on a number of findings relating to the design and use of mechanical indicators. The chapter closed with a discussion of illumination problems and with recommendations about the design of lighting systems for general and for certain specific purposes.

The next chapter continues with machine displays but concentrates on displays designed to be used by the other important channel of communication between man and machine—our sense of hearing.

chapter
four

Speech
Communication
Systems

Think of the many important ways in which aural signals help us to get along in our world of machines. The ringing of an alarm clock wakes us in the morning. The telephone rings. We answer it and talk with someone miles away. The wail of a siren warns us of the approach of an emergency vehicle. The purr—or, sometimes, the spasmodic wheezing and coughing—of our automobiles provides us with information about the functioning of their engines. These examples are only a few of the thousands of sounds, noises, and signals that assail our ears continually throughout the course of a day and communicate information to us aurally.

Aural communication systems can be grouped into two main classes: (a) tonal signaling systems (gongs, buzzers, bells, diaphones, horns, whistles, sirens, and other noises), and (b) speech communication systems. This chapter will be concerned only with speech communication systems, but some of the principles we find here will apply to tonal signaling systems as well.

The human factors involved in the design of speech communication systems may be grouped into three main categories:

1. Human engineering the language.

2. Human engineering the components of the communication system.

3. Human engineering the system as a whole.

The Basic Dimensions of Speech

Before we get into the specialized problems of speech communication systems, it is necessary to define the basic dimensions of speech. First, what is sound? In answering this question, we must keep in mind the distinction between (a) physical sound—the physical energy that makes up sound waves—and (b) the sensation that results when sound waves strike our ear drums, are transformed into nervous impulses, and are conveyed to our brains.

What Is Physical Sound?

The air around us is made up of millions of molecules not packed together very tightly. These molecules are in constant motion, but the movements are very small and often random in direction. If a solid object such as a piece of metal begins to vibrate, it changes the density or pressure of the air near it by alternately squeezing the molecules together and drawing them apart. When the air pressure is greater than normal, we speak of a *positive pressure;* when it is less than normal, we speak of a *negative pressure* (see Fig. 4–1). In a loudspeaker, the vibrating object is the speaker cone, activated by an electromagnet.

Pressure variations move through the air at a speed of about 760 miles per hour at sea level. The molecules of air move very little from their original positions, however, since any particular molecule is pulled back by the negative pressure almost as soon as it is pushed forward by the positive pressure. The only thing that really moves is the pressure wave.

When pressure waves hit the ear drum, they cause the ear drum to move. This movement in turn is transmitted to the inner parts of the ear and ultimately determines what you hear. How much the ear drum moves determines how loud the sound is, and how fast it moves determines the pitch. The two essential elements of sound are (a) how fast the changes in pressure occur (the *frequency*), and (b) how great the changes in pressure are (the *intensity*).

FREQUENCY

Many vibrating objects move back and forth in a very regular manner. For example, a tuning fork produces regular alternations in the pressure of the air because of its own regular movements (see Fig. 4–2). Variations of this type are called *sine waves,* and the sounds produced by such changes in pressure are called *pure tones* because they are generated by only a single vibration.

The frequency of a pure tone is defined by the number of cycles of pressure changes it goes through in a given period of time, usually a second. For example, if the pressure changes from positive to negative and back to positive five hundred times in one second, the frequency is 500 cycles per second (cps).

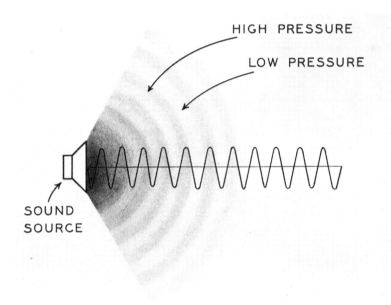

FIGURE 4–1. *A sound source emitting a pure tone produces alternations of high and low pressure in the air.*

INTENSITY

Another thing we need to know about a pure tone, or any sound, is its intensity, which is represented in Figure 4–2 as the *height* (or amplitude) of the sine wave. The human ear is a very sensitive instrument. It can hear sounds so weak that they are almost impossible to distinguish from the random movements of the air molecules. In fact, if the ear were much more sensitive than it is, people would hear these movements, which could be quite annoying. On the other hand, we hear sounds that may have an intensity 1,000,000,000,000,000 times as

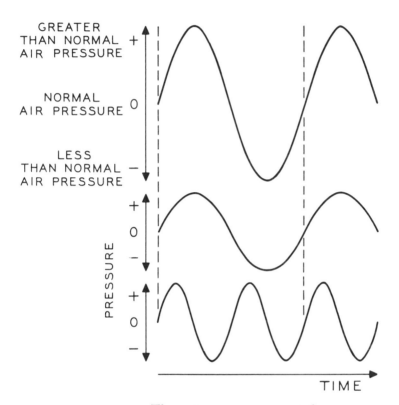

FIGURE 4–2. *These sine waves represent three pure tones. The tones corresponding to the top and middle waves have the same frequency but differ in intensity. The tones represented by the middle and bottom waves have the same intensity but differ in frequency. By comparing the number of full cycles between the broken lines you will find that the bottom wave has twice the frequency of the other two.*

great as that of the weakest sound we can hear. This range of sound intensities is so tremendous that engineeers have developed a special number scale to deal with them.

Sound intensities are normally measured in *decibels* (db), and can be defined in terms of *acoustic power* or *energy* or in terms of *sound pressures*. Since intensities (acoustic power or energy) and sound pressures are related in a simple way ($Po = cPr^2$), the following equations show how to compute decibels from either set of units:

$$\text{Number of decibels} = 10 \log_{10} \frac{Po_1}{Po_2} = 20 \log_{10} \frac{Pr_1}{Pr_2}$$

The decibel scale has two special features. First, it is a ratio measurement, and second, it is a logarithmic measurement. Table 4–1 shows some sample decibel computations and illustrates how logarithms compress some very large numbers into smaller ones.

TABLE 4–1. *Some computations using the decibel scale.*

SOUND PRESSURE OF SOUND 1	SOUND PRESSURE OF SOUND 2	$\dfrac{Pr_1}{Pr_2}$	$\log_{10} \dfrac{Pr_1}{Pr_2}$	$\dfrac{Po_1}{Po_2}$	$\log_{10} \dfrac{Po_1}{Po_2}$	NUMBER OF DECIBELS (db)
10	1	10	1	100	2	20
100	1	100	2	10,000	4	40
1,000	1	1,000	3	1,000,000	6	60
10,000	1	10,000	4	100,000,000	8	80
10,000	10	1,000	3	1,000,000	6	60

In order to provide the decibel scale with an absolute meaning, engineers use a certain reference pressure as a common anchor point. That reference pressure is 0.0002 dyne per square centimeter. It is very nearly equal to the minimum pressure the ear can hear under ideally quiet conditions. So defined, a sound-pressure level of 0 db corresponds approximately to the lowest audible intensity of a 1,000-cycle tone. Examples of intensity levels for some common sounds are shown in Figure 4–3.

Complex Sounds

Most sounds we hear are not pure tones. If the sound we are listening to is made up of relatively few pure tones and if the frequencies of these tones have certain fairly simple mathematical relations to

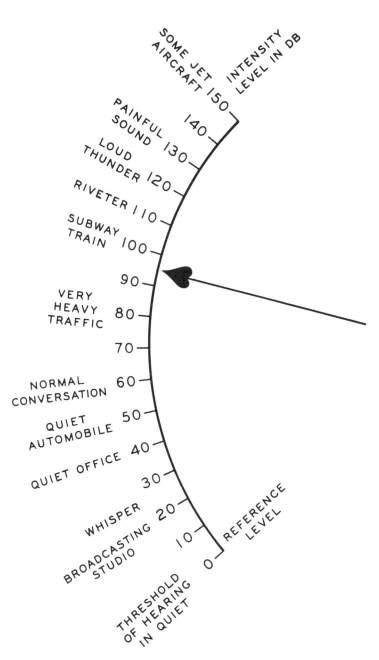

FIGURE 4-3. *The intensity levels of some familiar sounds. Most of the descriptive equivalents are approximate.*

one another, we would probably still describe the combination as a tone. But if the sound is made up of a great many frequencies, without any consistent relations among them, we would undoubtedly call the combination a noise. The main difference between noises and tones is that noises consist of many frequencies and intensities in a more or less unsystematic relation to each other. To describe such a complex sound or noise we usually plot its spectrum—a chart showing the combinations of all the frequencies and intensities that make it up. For example, Figure 4–4 shows a spectrum of the noise in a mechanical

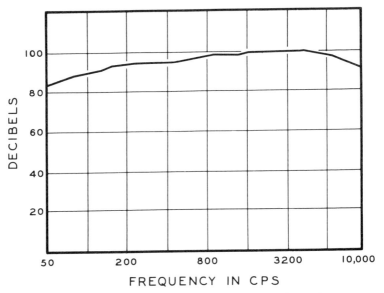

FIGURE 4–4.   *Spectrum of noise in a mechanical weaving mill.* (After Rüedi and Furrer, 26.)

weaving mill. We can see that this noise is made up of all the frequencies from 50 to 10,000 cps. Although the frequencies with the highest intensities are in the vicinity of 2,000 to 5,000 cps, the spectrum is very nearly uniform throughout.

WHITE NOISE

A special kind of noise that is useful in auditory experimentation is called "white noise." It is analogous to white light in that it consists of all frequencies represented in equal intensities. If the spectrum of white noise were to be drawn in a plot such as shown in Figure 4–4, it would be a flat line parallel to the abscissa. The noise that an air jet makes is a good example of a noise with a nearly flat spectrum, and it sounds nearly like white noise. White noise is commonly created in acoustic laboratories as a background noise against which many types of speech-intelligibility experiments are run.

SPEECH-TO-NOISE RATIO

The speech-to-noise ratio, commonly abbreviated as S/N, is a measure of the relative intensity (or sound-pressure level) of the speech to the noise in a noisy environment. For example, if the average intensity of speech is 90 db and the average intensity of the noise in which the speech is spoken is 70 db, we have an S/N ratio of $+20$ db. If the average intensity of the speech is 70 db and it is heard in an environment with an overall noise level of 70 db, the S/N ratio is 0 db. If the average intensity of the speech is 60 db and it is heard in a noisy environment with the noise at 70 db, the S/N ratio is -10 db. To compute the S/N ratio, subtract the number of decibels in the noise from the number of decibels in the signal or speech. Remember that decibels are logarithms. To take the ratio of two numbers, subtract their logarithms.

Human Engineering the Language

What do we mean by the expression *human engineering the language?* We mean that if you know the conditions under which a communication system will be used and can describe or define the noise conditions in which speech will be heard, it is usually possible to construct a specialized language to help improve the intelligibility of the speech.

Size of Vocabulary

One important way of increasing the intelligibility of language in the presence of noise is to limit the size of the vocabulary. If the number of words to be transmitted over a noisy communication channel is kept small, and if the entire list of these words is known to both the listener and the talker, the chances of successfully communicating are greatly increased. Figure 4–5 shows an experiment conducted by having a talker say words into a microphone, the words being delivered to a listener through a set of earphones. White noise was introduced at

the listener's earphones. The signal-to-noise ratio was varied by changing the level of the noise. The chief experimental variable was the
size of the vocabulary. The listener was told that each test word would
be one of the items from a certain restricted vocabulary. The size
of this vocabulary was either 2, 4, 8, 16, 32, or 256 words. The
data labeled "monosyllables" were collected by using a list of 1,000

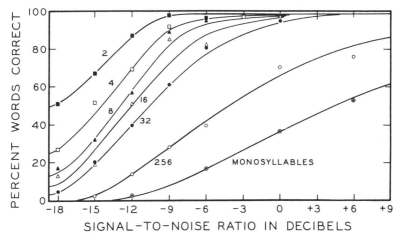

FIGURE 4–5. *Intelligibility of monosyllables as
a function of the size of the vocabulary. The 2
identifies the data obtained when the listener
had to hear one of two possible words. The 4
identifies the data obtained when the listener
had to hear words from a vocabulary of four
words. And so on. The curve labeled "monosyllables" is data for a vocabulary of 1,000
monosyllables. (After Miller, Heise, and Lichten,
24.)*

monosyllables which the listener did not know in advance. In any
event, the talker always spoke words from one of these lists.

The words used in these vocabularies were chosen at random from
a special list of phonetically balanced monosyllables. For the 2-
alternative vocabulary different pairs of words were chosen and typed
on the listener's answer sheet. The talker read one word of the pairs of
words and the listener checked the item that he thought he had heard.
A similar procedure was used for the 4- and 8-word vocabularies. For
the 16-, 32-, and 256-word vocabularies, the listener had a list of all

the words in front of him, and he could study the list until he made a choice. After the choice was made and recorded, a signal was given to the talker to go on to the next item.

The results show clearly that the size of the vocabulary is an important factor contributing to the perception of speech in noise. When the vocabulary is very large (the monosyllable curve) and the signal-to-noise ratio is −12 decibels, scarcely 2 per cent of the words can be heard correctly. If the vocabulary is restricted to one of 16 words, however, about 50 per cent of the words can be heard correctly. If the choice is further restricted to one of 2 words, about 90 per cent of the words can be heard correctly.

The data in Figure 4–5 are not corrected for chance, which means that when the listener has a 2-word vocabulary the probability is 0.5 that he will get words correct merely by guessing. However, even after the appropriate corrections are made for the probabilities of guessing, the difference between the 2-word and 1,000-word vocabularies still amounts to a factor of about 18 decibels. That is a very large effect.

The Context in Which the Word Appears

Another factor influencing the intelligibility of speech in noise is the context in which the words are heard. A word is much harder to understand if it is heard in isolation than if it is heard in a sentence. This fact is illustrated by Figure 4–6. Sentences containing five key words were read and the listeners' responses were scored by computing the percentage of the key words heard correctly. For comparison, the key words were abstracted from the sentences, scrambled, and reread singly. As you can see, words can be heard much more readily in sentences than alone. You have undoubtedly used this trick on certain occasions to make yourself intelligible over the telephone or perhaps in trying to communicate with a partially deaf person. When you are trying to convey the word "fire" and your listener keeps thinking you are saying "flyer," an effective way of getting your meaning across is to say something like "No, not flyer! Fire, as in 'Your house is on fire.' "

A Word-Spelling Alphabet

When communication links are poor because of distance or atmospheric conditions, or the noise is excessively great, it is sometimes necessary to spell out each word you are trying to communicate. Although this procedure is tedious and time consuming, it is very effective. Its effectiveness can be increased by making each letter into a word. This technique is known as *word spelling*. A considerable amount of research has gone into getting a suitable list of words for this purpose. Among other things, such words should be easy to pronounce,

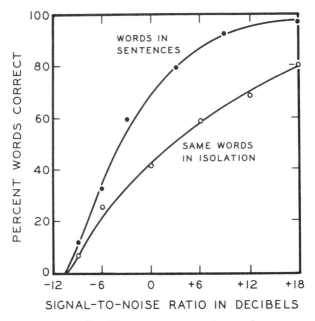

FIGURE 4-6. *The upper curve shows the proportion of key words that could be correctly identified in sentences read over a noisy communication channel. The lower curve shows the proportion of the same words that could be heard correctly when the key words were read singly over the same communication channel.* (After Miller, Heise, and Lichten, 24.)

readable by persons with all sorts of educational backgrounds, and easily distinguishable from one another. An additional requirement was placed on such a list for military use, because of our participation in the North Atlantic Treaty Organization: the words needed to be recognizable when spoken by and to persons of different nationalities and accents. Finding a list to satisfy all these requirements was no easy task. The years of research done on this problem resulted in the final outcome shown in Table 4-2.

TABLE 4-2. *International word-spelling alphabet adopted by the International Civil Aviation Organization (ICAO).*

Alpha	November
Bravo	Oscar
Charlie	Papa
Delta	Quebec
Echo	Romeo
Foxtrot	Sierra
Golf	Tango
Hotel	Uniform
India	Victor
Juliet	Whiskey
Kilo	X Ray
Lima	Yankee
Mike	Zulu

The alphabet in Table 4-2 is now officially adopted by the NATO nations for communications purposes. To transmit the word *hotdog,* for example, the talker says, "Hotel, Oscar, Tango, Delta, Oscar, Golf." One of the reasons this alphabet is so effective is that it makes use of a principle discussed above; namely, that of using a restricted vocabulary known to both talker and listener. In addition to being a restricted vocabulary, this is a specially selected one, full of context and redundancy for getting the maximum amount of information across.

Summary of Principles

The following factors should be considered in designing a language to be used under adverse conditions:

1. Pick words with a minimum of easily confused sounds. (Although we have not specifically discussed this problem here, a considerable amount of research is available on the sounds that are most easily confused and those that are most readily distinguished under noisy conditions. See, for example, Morgan et al., 25.)

2. Use as small a vocabulary as possible and make sure that this vocabulary is known to all the communicators.

3. Use familiar rather than unfamiliar words. (See tabulations of the most frequently used words in the English language in Thorndike and Lorge, 30.)

4. Supply as much context for your words as possible. Put the difficult ones in a sentence if you can.

5. If communication is extremely difficult, use the word-spelling technique with the alphabet in Table 4-2.

Human Engineering the Components of Speech Communication Systems

We turn now to the human engineering of the machine components used in speech communication systems. In this connection, I shall highlight only one of several principles and emphasize ways of making speech more intelligible in noisy places.

Amplitude Selectivity

One important way in which the intelligibility of speech may be affected is by the selective action of components of the communication system on the speech wave itself. In essence, the system may discriminate against certain parts or features of the speech signal and favor others. This selective action may occur in any of several places—in the transmission medium, in the microphone, in the amplifiers, or in the loudspeaker—and may discriminate against any of the basic variables of the speech wave, that is, against frequency, amplitude, or time. A commonplace example of frequency selectivity is found in cheap radios and record players. In these cases, the selectivity is not deliberately designed into the system but is there because of the nature of the components that are used. To avoid the frequency selectivity arising from this source (that is, to get a record player with a flat response), you have to buy special, so-called *hi-fi* components.

PEAK AND CENTER CLIPPING

Peak clipping discriminates against the high-amplitude parts of the speech wave by eliminating all those amplitudes that exceed a certain value. Center clipping eliminates all those amplitudes below a certain value. Since both peak and center clipping produce severe mutilations of the speech wave, they are commonly called *amplitude distortion*. Both types of amplitude distortion are illustrated in Figure 4-7. There you see at the top of the illustration a schematic

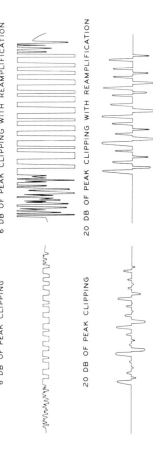

ORIGINAL
SPEECH WAVE

J .... O E

6 DB OF PEAK CLIPPING   6 DB OF PEAK CLIPPING WITH REAMPLIFICATION

20 DB OF PEAK CLIPPING   20 DB OF PEAK CLIPPING WITH REAMPLIFICATION

6 DB OF CENTER CLIPPING   6 DB OF CENTER CLIPPING WITH REAMPLIFICATION

FIGURE 4-7.   *The speech wave at the top is a schematic representation of the wave form when a male voice speaks the word Joe. The tracings at the left show what remains after various amounts of peak or center clipping. The corresponding tracings on the right show what the speech waves look like when they are each reamplified to the same intensity as the original speech wave. (After Licklider, Bindra, and Pollack, 20.)*

representation of the wave form resulting when a male voice says the word *Joe*. Notice that there is first a series of low-amplitude, high-frequency vibrations corresponding to the *J* sound (not the sound *Jay* that is pronounced in the alphabet but the sound *J* as pronounced in the word *Joe*). These are followed by high-amplitude, lower-frequency vibrations corresponding to the O sound.

Start to say the word *Joe*, but do not pronounce the O sound. Now pronounce the O sound. Do this carefully several times, and you will notice that the O sound is much louder than the *J* sound—it has much more intensity, or amplitude. In addition, the O sound is lower, or deeper, than the *J* sound—that is, it has a lower pitch, or a lower base frequency. The uppermost tracing in Figure 4–7 shows these two facts in terms of the sound waves involved.

Now imagine that we have a mechanism that chops off the highest peaks of the sound wave, as illustrated by the dotted lines in Figure 4–7. If we let the original amplitude of the speech wave, A_o, be equal to 1, then the clipped wave shown here has an amplitude, A_c, of 0.5. To find out how many decibels this represents, put these numbers into the following equation and work out the answer as below:

$$N_{(db)} = 20 \log_{10} \frac{A_c}{A_o} = 20 \log_{10} \frac{0.5}{1}$$

$$= 20 \log_{10} (0.5) = 20 (\bar{1}.699)$$

$$= 20 (-0.301) = -6.02.$$

To sum up, when we chop off half the speech wave, we subject the wave to about 6 decibels of peak clipping. Figure 4–7 also shows 20 decibels of peak clipping. With this much peak clipping, about nine-tenths of the speech wave is cut off and discarded. If you would like some practice in using the decibel formula, verify this last statement for yourself.

How far can we go in peak clipping? Theoretically, the answer is that we can carry peak clipping until we are left only with square waves (*infinite peak clipping*). Actually, it is impossible to get infinite peak clipping, but Figure 4–8 shows what infinite peak clipping would look like in the ideal case. Notice that every time the original speech wave crosses the "zero" baseline a square wave is generated in that direction. The result is that all wave form is destroyed and all amplitudes are identical.

The opposite of peak clipping is *center clipping*. Instead of cut-

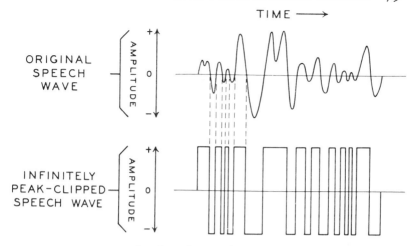

FIGURE 4–8. *Speech can be transformed into square waves by a circuit that generates an electric signal whenever the original wave crosses the "zero" axis. This circuit produces infinite peak clipping.*

ting off the peaks, we cut out the center part of the wave and leave the peaks, joining them together as shown in Figure 4–7.

INTELLIGIBILITY OF CLIPPED SPEECH

As we noted at the beginning of this section, clipped speech is mutilated speech. We should expect, therefore, to lose something in the understandability of the speech when we distort it in this way. The results of numerous experiments show that peak clipping affects the quality and the naturalness of the speech but, surprisingly enough, it has little effect on its understandability (see Fig. 4–9). For example, with as much as 24 decibels of peak clipping (that is, when fifteen-sixteenths of the speech wave is cut away) more than 95 per cent of monosyllabic words can still be heard correctly. Even with infinite peak clipping we can still hear correctly about 70 per cent of ordinary monosyllabic words, which is surprisingly good!

Now, contrast this intelligibility with what happens when the speech is subjected to center clipping (the dotted line in Fig. 4–9). Clipping out only a quarter of the speech wave (2.5 decibels) reduces the understandability of speech to about 30 per cent; clipping out half of the wave (6 decibels of center clipping) makes speech almost entirely unintelligible.

The explanation for this rather unusual state of affairs involves some interesting facts about speech and speech sounds. The low-intensity components of the speech wave are the semi-vowels and consonants. The high-intensity parts of the speech waves consist of the vowels and diphthongs. Some vowels (for example, the *aw* sound in *jaw* or the *a* in *calm*), as used in ordinary conversation, have over 1,000 times the average speech power of some consonants (for example,

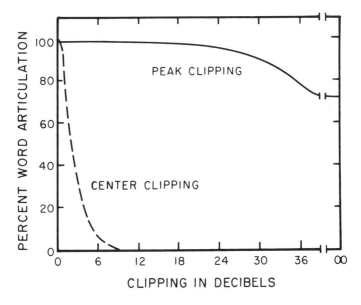

FIGURE 4–9. *The intelligibility of speech that has been subjected to peak and center clipping in various amounts.* (After Licklider and Miller, 21.)

the *v* in *vine*). To take another example, it is very difficult to hiss in a loud voice, but easy to shout "O."

When we peak-clip speech waves, we are essentially cutting off some of the power of the vowel sounds. This is not very disastrous, because the vowel sounds do not contribute very much to the understandability of speech. The consonant sounds are more important for producing understandable speech. We can also see now why center clipping has such dire consequences. When we center-clip the speech wave, we are discriminating against those important consonant sounds.

To get some intuitive notion of the relative importance of the vowels and consonants, try to pronounce the two mutilated sentences in this paragraph. The first has had all its consonants replaced by the letter f; the second has had all its vowels replaced by the letter o. Which is the harder to read and understand? Fafiff aff foffofafff afife feaffy fefufef ffe iffeffiffififfy of ffeeff. O somolor oporotoon on tho vowols os not so sorooos.

PEAK CLIPPING WITH REAMPLIFICATION

We have still not come to the interesting and important part of our story—improving the intelligibility of speech in noise. As Figure 4–7 shows, when we peak-clip speech, we also reduce the average amount of power; clipped speech is not as loud as unclipped speech. Suppose, however, that we were to reamplify the clipped speech until it had the same peak intensity as the unclipped speech. The illustrations on the right of Figure 4–7 show what these reamplified waves would look like. This procedure is a sensible one from an engineering point of view since there are many communication systems which have a limited amplitude-handling capacity. What we are doing is making better use of this capacity. By clipping the speech and reamplifying it, we are chopping off some of the intensity of the vowel sounds and expanding the intensity of the consonant sounds. This amounts to increasing the average power of the speech wave while holding its peak amplitude constant.

Figure 4–10 tells us how much we gain by this operation. The data were obtained after putting the talker in a quiet room and the listener in a noisy one. The listener tried to understand (a) unclipped speech at various peak amplitudes, and (b) speech that had been clipped by various amounts and reamplified to various peak amplitudes. Take for example, the data for a peak amplitude of 80 decibels. Under the noise conditions in which these particular tests were made, the average listener could get scarcely 1 per cent of the unclipped words that were spoken. But with 12 decibels of peak clipping, the average listener could hear and understand about 40 per cent of the words, and with 24 decibels of peak clipping, approximately three-fourths of the words. This difference is an impressive gain in intelligibility.

This general principle has wide applicability. It has been put to good use in the design of radio transmitters where the amplitude-handling capacity of the system is limited by the amount of modulation possible on the carrier signal. Another application is in the design of hearing aids where the peak amplitude is limited by a psychological consideration—if the amplitude is too great, it tickles the ear, or it may even become uncomfortable or painful.

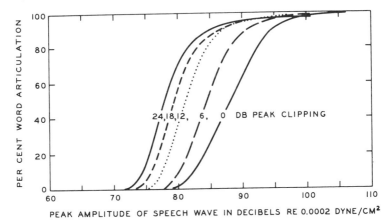

FIGURE 4–10.   *The intelligibility of clipped and unclipped speech in a noisy environment. When clipped and unclipped speech have the same peak-to-peak amplitude, clipped speech is more audible.* (After Licklider, 19.)

Human Factors in the Design and Selection of Components

This section summarizes a few additional human-engineering principles governing the design and selection of components for speech communication systems. These principles are listed without explanation primarily because of limitations of space. If you are interested in fuller explanations of how and why they work, consult Morgan et al. (25).

> 1. When noise levels are high (about 80 db or more) or when speech levels are high (about 85 db or more), ear plugs or some comparable kind of ear-protective device will usually improve speech intelligibility in face-to-face communication.

2. In selecting microphones, look for those that (a) have high sensitivity to acoustic speech signals, (b) transduce acoustic signals faithfully, and (c) reject other acoustic signals and noises at the speaker's location (so-called noise-canceling microphones).

3. If the noise surrounding the talker is negligible or moderate, an automatic gain control (AGC) after the microphone will often improve intelligibility. If the system has an appreciable amount of internal noise, an AGC in the receiver will usually help.

4. When the noise surrounding the speaker is very high, inserting a high-pass filter (with an attenuation of about 6 db per octave) in a speech communication system after the microphone will help reduce high-frequency noise and improve speech intelligibility.

5. If the speech communication system has an appreciable amount of internal noise, consider the use of a peak limiter in the receiver.

6. Use loudspeakers rather than headsets when (a) environmental-noise levels are low, (b) listeners must move around or would otherwise be hampered by wires and cables, or (c) many listeners must hear the message.

7. Use headsets rather than loudspeakers when (a) environment-noise levels are high, (b) different listeners must hear different messages, (c) reverberation in the room is a serious problem, (d) the listener must wear special equipment (such as an oxygen mask), or (e) the power output is too low to operate a loudspeaker.

Engineering the System as a Whole

We turn now to some of the broader problems of engineering communication systems in their entirety. Communication systems sometimes have to be used under unusual circumstances—for example, at high altitudes or underwater—and the design of systems of this type sometimes requires using components in ways which normally would not be most effective.

Multichannel Listening

A special situation in the design of communication systems arises from the difficulties of multichannel listening. For instance, imagine yourself in the air-traffic-control tower of a large modern airport. Around you are a number of loudspeakers, which from time to time emit messages from nearby stations, from the weather office, and from pilots in the vicinity of the airport. Since all of these messages are important at various times none of them can be turned off. Yet your task at a particular moment may be to hear, and to hear correctly, the message from one particular pilot. At the same time, as you are trying to do this critical listening, there may be other voices speaking, competing for your attention. This is the problem of multichannel listening. It occurs in a variety of communication centers—aboard ships, in message centers, and in offices from which taxis are dispatched by radio.

This problem has certain points of similarity to the problem of *masking* by noise—where the listener is trying to receive a message in the presence of a competing noise—except that the noise, in multichannel listening, is another voice. It is this last factor that makes multichannel listening a little more complicated than simply listening to a voice in the presence of random noise. What often happens is that the listener starts out listening to the words in one message, but somewhere in the middle—without even realizing it—finds himself listening to the words in another message. You have had first-hand experience with this problem if you have ever tried to carry on a conversation at a cocktail party where a lot of people around you were trying to carry on simultaneous conversations.

Can engineering help the listener under such circumstances? To answer this question we shall summarize briefly two experiments which give some constructive suggestions about improving our ability to listen to some messages in the presence of others.

FREQUENCY FILTERING AND SEPARATION OF LOUDSPEAKERS

The first experiment was conducted at the Naval Electronics Laboratory. Figure 4–11 contains a simplified diagram of the plan of the experiment. First, these investigators had a three-channel, magnetic-film playback equipment. Each of the three channels carried a different message. They were called Channel Able, Channel Baker, and Channel Charlie.

The voice on Channel Able went directly to a switch at point S_1. The voice on Channel Baker, however, could be shunted at point S_2 through either of two paths. If it went through the line marked

OUT, the voice was unmodified—that is, it came out in the same form as the voice on Channel Able. If the switch at point S_2 were turned to IN, then the voice on Channel Baker went through a high-pass filter which passed frequencies above 1,600 cycles per second and rejected frequencies below 1,600 cycles per second. This is a frequency-selective filter. It has the effects of increasing the pitch of the voice and of discriminating against the vowel sounds. Channel Charlie could be subjected to similar alternatives: it could be passed unmodified (when the switch S_3 was in the OUT position), or it could be passed through a low-pass filter with a cutoff at 1,600 cycles per second.

At point S_1 the three voices, or channels, could be subjected to still further alternatives. When the switch was up (as in the figure), all three voices were fed to the same loudspeaker. When the switch

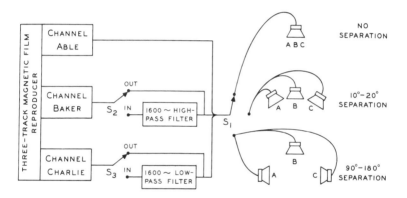

FIGURE 4-11. *A schematic diagram of the multichannel-listening experiment conducted by Spieth and his co-workers (27).*

was thrown to the middle position, the three voices were separated and fed into three separate loudspeakers, A, B, and C. A and B were separated by 10°, B and C were also separated by 10°, but A and C were separated by 20°. When the switch at S_1 was thrown to the lowest position, the three voices were again each fed to separate loudspeakers, but the loudspeakers were separated by 90°; that is, A and B were 90° apart, B and C were also 90° apart, but A and C were 180° apart.

There were two separate tasks which the subjects in this experiment had to do. Each subject was told something like this: "Your code name is Oboe. You are to listen only for messages which start with this code name. When you hear a message which is intended for you, tell me first over which channel the message came. Then answer the question which the message asks you." The difficulty, of course, was that two channels always came on at the same time. A sample pair of messages might be something like this:

> *Channel Able:* Oboe, this is Able 2. Where in box 5 is the triangle? Over.
>
> *Channel Baker:* King, this is Baker 1. What box contains two circles? Over.

The questions were always so simple that there was no real problem following instructions; the problem was trying to untangle the relevant question from the question being asked on the competing channel.

The voices always came in pairs. One-third of the time they came over Channels Able and Baker, one-third of the time over Channels Able and Charlie, and one-third over Channels Baker and Charlie.

The results of the two different tasks (that is, identifying the channel or answering the question) are so nearly the same that we shall only consider one set of data—those relating to the percentage of questions answered correctly. These results are shown in Figure 4–12.

First, look at the effect of separating the speakers without modifying the channels. These data are shown by the lower curve (broken line) in Figure 4–12. When the three voices came on in the same loudspeaker, the listeners were able to answer only about 65 per cent of the questions. Separating the speakers by only 10° produced a marked improvement. Separating the speakers further produced still further improvement.

Now look at what happens when the frequency-selective filters were put into the circuits. When the voices came over the same loudspeaker and the voices were unmodified, the listeners could get only about 65 per cent of the questions. When all three channels were fed into the same loudspeaker and two of the voices passed through frequency-selective filters, the percentage went up to about 85 per cent. When the speakers were separated by 10° or 20°, frequency-selective filters improved reception by about 5 per cent over the results obtained with unmodified voices. When the speakers were separated by 90° or 180° there was no added improvement from using the filters.

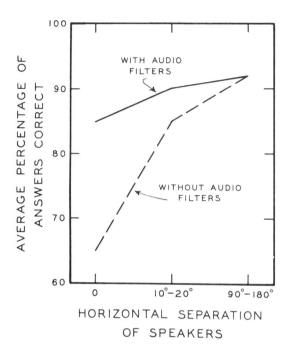

FIGURE 4–12. *Results obtained in the multi-channel-listening experiment diagrammed in Figure 4–11. Separating the speakers makes it easier to listen to one of two competing messages. Additional help can be provided by passing the voices through frequency-selective filters.* (After Spieth et al., 27.)

MONAURAL VERSUS DICHOTIC LISTENING

The second experiment was made by Egan and his collaborators at Indiana University (10). They, like the Navy investigators, tested the effects of several design factors on multichannel listening. But we shall look at only one of the experimental comparisons they made, one that concerns the difference between monaural and dichotic listening.

Monaural means one-eared; the message or messages are fed into one ear. *Binaural* means two-eared; messages are fed into both ears at the same time. Binaural listening is the kind you normally indulge in. *Dichotic* refers to a special kind of two-eared listening: one voice is fed into one ear, but another voice is fed into the other ear. Thus, in binaural listening both ears hear the same thing; in dichotic listening one ear hears one thing, the other ear hears another.

Since the design of Egan's experiment is quite different from the one we have just reviewed, it requires a few words of explanation. First, two different kinds of listening were compared—monaural and dichotic. In the monaural trials, both the speech and the interference were presented to the same ear through an earphone. In the dichotic trials, one earphone presented the speech; the other, the interference. Second, two kinds of interference were used: (a) random noise and (b) connected discourse spoken by the voice that was used to record the speech signal. The speech to which the observer was supposed to listen consisted of selections from *The Wealth of Nations* by Adam Smith. At the start of any trial, the interference was set to a certain intensity and the subject was asked to turn up the intensity of the speech until he could hear and understand it. The results of these tests are shown in Figure 4–13.

Note that the baseline in the figure gives the sound-pressure level of the interfering signal. The higher this value, the louder the interfering signal. The ordinate of the graph tells us the sound-pressure level of the received signal that could just be heard. Higher values along this scale mean that the speech had to be turned up louder in order to be heard. In general, you can see that when the interfering signal increased in intensity, subjects had to turn up the intensity of the speech signal in order to hear it. But notice the very large difference between the data for monaural and dichotic listening. With dichotic presentation, the curves are nearly flat. The interfering signal could be increased over a very large range of values with hardly any effect on the subject's ability to hear the speech. In monaural listening, on the other hand, the intensity of the received signal had to be increased greatly in order to make it audible over the interfering signal.

The superiority of dichotic over monaural listening is consistent with the findings obtained in experiments on the separation of loudspeakers. Such experiments show that best results are obtained when loudspeakers are separated 180°, so that one speaker faces each ear. Dichotic listening is, in a manner of speaking, a special case of this condition. In dichotic listening, the speakers are separated 180° and are brought so close that they touch the ears.

One minor point of interest concerns the difference between the

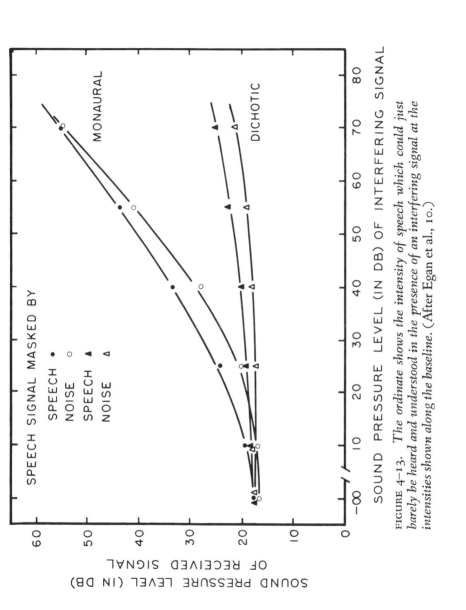

FIGURE 4-13.   *The ordinate shows the intensity of speech which could just barely be heard and understood in the presence of an interfering signal at the intensities shown along the baseline.* (After Egan et al., 10.)

two kinds of interfering signals. Although the differences are not very large, mere noise was not so effective an interfering signal as was connected discourse.

RECOMMENDATIONS ABOUT MULTICHANNEL LISTENING

Whenever listeners have to identify and understand spoken messages in the presence of competing messages, the designer can help by:

1. Providing frequency-selective circuits: voice channels can be given distinctive qualities by passing them through high-pass, low-pass, or band-pass filters.

2. Separating the speakers that carry different messages.

3. Designing dichotic rather than monaural or binaural listening.

4. Keeping the average intensity of the voice channels at somewhat different levels. If the message to be heard is slightly more intense than the message to be ignored, you would expect an improvement in efficiency because of the more favorable S/N ratio. If the message to be received is somewhat less intense than the one to be ignored, the distinctiveness created by the intensity difference offsets the masking of the less intense by the more intense voice.

5. Delaying some messages so that they are not synchronous with other messages.

6. Providing a facility, such as a selector switch, that enables the listener to transfer the desired message from any loudspeaker to an earphone or special loudspeaker near him.

Some Considerations for Systems Design

The human factors engineer should keep in mind the following considerations when he designs a communication system.

1. Speech communication is best when noise levels in the environment of the talker and listener are low. Whenever possible, excessive noise should be stopped at the source by such methods as damping noisy machinery, or by muffling or deflecting the noise with insulation, sound-baffles, or ear-protective devices.

2. Excessive sound reverberation in auditoriums, classrooms, and

conference rooms is another enemy of communication and should be reduced to acceptable levels (below one second for classrooms and conference rooms). Reverberation may be decreased by using several or many low-powered loudspeakers distributed throughout the area instead of a few powerful loudspeakers. It also helps if the loudspeakers are directional and oriented to cover the major parts of the room with minimal overlap in coverage among them.

3. For high-quality sound reproduction, the *dynamic range* (the difference between the sound-pressure level at which *overload* occurs in the system and the sound-pressure level of noise in the system) should be 60 db. For lower-quality reproduction, roughly comparable to that of commercial broadcast, the dynamic range can be 40 to 45 db. If the system has some mechanism (such as *AGC*) to compensate for variations in average speech levels among talkers, a dynamic range of 30 db will allow nearly perfect speech intelligibility. If highly practiced talkers and listeners will be used in the communication system, a dynamic range as low as 20 db is satisfactory.

4. Speech communication systems should provide *feedback* to the talker. Examples of feedback are (a) the dial tone in a telephone, which tells the caller that the system is prepared to accept his call, (b) the ringing sound that tells the talker that the system has accepted and is processing his call, and (c) "Roger, wilco, and out" from the person at the other end of the communication system. Feedback is important to tell the talker that the system is operating properly, that the listener has received his message, that his message has been correctly understood, and that the listener has taken appropriate action on the message. Feedback, in short, is a way of assuring both the talker and the listener that two-way communication really exists. This knowledge in itself has been shown to give a considerable boost in morale to both the talker and the listener, particularly in emergency communications.

Summary

This chapter has been entirely concerned with speech communication systems. An introductory section defined the basic dimensions of speech and the units in which we measure and describe speech quantitatively. We saw next that the basic human factors problems could be classed roughly into three categories: (a) human engineering the language, (b) human engineering the components of the communication system, and (c) engineering the system as a whole. Numerous research studies show that impressive gains can be made in the effectiveness of speech communication systems through proper design of the elements of the system and of the system as a whole.

With this chapter we conclude our discussion of machine displays. The next chapter takes us to the other side of the man-machine loop, to the design of controls and of the instruments by which man communicates his instructions to machines and machine systems.

chapter five

The Design
of Controls

The last two chapters have been concerned with sensory inputs
to the human operator—with ways in which machines convey information to their human counterparts. But our model of the man-machine
system (Fig. 2–2) shows that the linkages between human operators
and machines are two-directional. The operator who receives information from machines often acts upon this information through some
sort of control—pushbuttons, knobs, cranks, levers, switches, wheels,
and pedals are some of the more common ones.

What are the human factors that determine which control is
most appropriate for a specific function? What important variables
should the human factors engineer consider in designing such controls? Where should controls be located? These and related questions
shall be our concern in this chapter.

Some Common Troubles with Controls

What sorts of problems do people have with controls? If we
know the kinds of mistakes people typically make in using controls,
we will be in a much better position to design more nearly foolproof
devices.

A classic study of this question was made by Fitts and Jones
(11) just after World War II. They investigated errors made in
operating aircraft controls but their findings are much more general.
The difficulties they found among aircraft controls apply equally
well to controls for automobiles, machine tools, and stoves. In addition
to its engineering and scientific merits, the Fitts and Jones report con-

tains some dramatic incidents that are worth quoting at some length. But first, a look at its background.

The investigation was started in December 1945 to discover if some of the many so-called "pilot-error" accidents might be traced to faulty design features. Some five hundred pilots and former pilots were given this assignment:

> Describe in detail an error in the operation of a cockpit control (flight control, engine control, toggle switch, selector switch, trim-tab control, etc.) which was made by yourself or by another person whom you were watching at the time.

Some of the pilots did not answer the question and some described errors that were due entirely to mechanical failure or to errors of judgment. When these were eliminated, 460 usable replies remained. The stories contained in these replies were carefully studied to discover the psychological features of each incident that contributed to the error. This analysis showed that many of the incidents had important common elements. As a result, the investigators were able to group the incidents into six major categories. Examination of the aircraft involved in the incidents also led Fitts and Jones to make a series of recommendations for design changes that would be most likely to reduce the likelihood of pilots making errors of each type. But the stories speak for themselves.

Here is one incident in the pilot's own words:

> This error occurred in a C-47 aircraft. The pilot, after the usual procedure of lowering the gear and other landing checks, turned on the final approach leg and reduced power. Shortly afterwards, he found it necessary to increase power to avoid undershooting. In reaching for the throttle, the pilot grasped the propeller control. Advancing the prop control, the engines sounded as if power were being applied. This occurred far enough out on the approach so that corrective action prevented an accident. However, had this error occurred closer to the ground, an accident might have occurred. The pilot was familiar with the control panel of a B-25; hence, he automatically grasped the set of controls nearest, or in other words, those on the left side.

An important psychological observation is contained in the last sentence of this story. Let's look at what was involved. Three aircraft in common use at the time of this study were the B-25, the C-47, and the C-82. The arrangement of three critical controls in each of these aircraft is as follows:

	CONTROL PLACEMENT ON THE THROTTLE QUADRANT		
AIRCRAFT	LEFT	CENTER	RIGHT
B-25	Throttle	Propeller	Mixture
C-47	Propeller	Throttle	Mixture
C-82	Mixture	Throttle	Propeller

Now that we have these data before us, the pilot's action seems much less careless.

Landing an aircraft is one of the most tension-producing phases of normal flight. The pilot is busy watching the ground to avoid obstacles and to be sure that he will not over- or undershoot the runway, watching for other air traffic, and glancing at critical flight instruments to check on the performance of his aircraft. A slight lapse of attention or error of judgment at this stage might easily mean a collision or crash.

Put yourself in the place of a pilot who had been flying a B-25 for hundreds of hours. You're busy looking around, you see that you need a little more power, you reach for the throttle in its old familiar place—after all, hundreds of hours of experience have taught you where to find that throttle by touch and feel alone—*but the throttle isn't there!*

Let's put this problem into a different context. If you have been driving a car with a standard transmission for any appreciable length of time, you have learned to brake with one foot and to use the clutch with the other. If you have been driving for many years, you will probably have to think a moment before you can recall exactly which foot does what. Driving is so automatic—so *overlearned,* as psychologists might say—that it is almost a reflex action requiring no conscious thought or control. Now imagine what might happen if you were to try to drive a car in which the brake and clutch pedals were reversed!

If you have an automobile with an automatic transmission, it may have control settings identified as "Park," "Neutral," "Reverse," "Low," and "Drive." I said *may* because some cars have different and some have fewer alternatives than these. Have you ever borrowed a friend's car and become confused because the controls on his automobile were arranged differently? When you become confused in an automobile, you can pull over to the side of the road and stop to regain your composure. The aircraft pilot, however, does not have time for a leisurely appraisal of the situation.

Here is a story which points up another sort of difficulty:

> This was a case of mistaking prop pitch controls for throttle controls in a C-47 while the pilot was flying a GCA. We were on the final approach at about 600 feet when we noticed an unusual sound in the engines. What had happened was that the pilot had taken hold of the prop controls and was using them for throttles. They were next to the pilot while the throttles were in the center. This was a bad installation also, because the gauge for the props was on the right of the manifold-pressure gauge while the prop controls were on the left of the throttle controls.

Here, again, the pilot reporting the incident has made an astute observation—one that concerns the problem of display-control arrangement. Among other things, advancing the throttle increases the engine manifold pressure, which is displayed on the manifold-pressure gauge. The propeller pitch control changes the pitch of the propeller blades, which changes the number of revolutions per minute (RPM) of the engine. In the C-47, the manifold-pressure gauge was on the left of the RPM indicator. But the controls associated with these two indicators were reversed, so that the throttle was on the right of the propeller pitch control.

Following are two incidents involving other errors:

> 1. On a routine combat mission, a recently checked-out co-pilot flying as first pilot had been given a position as wing man. As they were going over the target, an engine was damaged by flak and heated up and lost considerable oil. Therefore, he had his co-pilot feather the engine. He remained in formation over the target and all the way home. On arriving at the field, he requested the co-pilot to unfeather this damaged engine . . . [An argument developed] . . . and finally the first pilot became angry and reached for the feathering button. He hit the wrong one, feathering the second engine. At this time, both pilots put their heads in the cockpit, trying to get their engines un-

feathered. All this time, they were still in formation. As a result of concentrating on the unfeathering procedure, they skidded into the flight leader, cutting his fuselage off just in front of the vertical stabilizer; and his plane plummeted to the earth 1,000 feet below, killing the eleven occupants.

2. My P-51 squadron was making the first fighter-escort mission from Iwo Jima to Japan as escort for a strike force of B-29's. All went well until we reached the rendezvous point with the bombers just south of the mouth of Tokyo Bay. At this point, the signal was given for the fighters to drop external gas tanks. My altitude at this time was 21,000 feet. Before dropping, I switched to an internal tank in the prescribed manner. When I pulled the manual release for the extra gas tanks, only one tank dropped, so I gave the release another and harder pull. Almost immediately, my engine cut out without warning. I called the flight leader, told him of my trouble, and turned out toward the ocean, for by that time we were about 30 miles inland . . .

I was very puzzled as to the trouble with my engine and did not find the trouble until I was down to 9,000 feet and all by myself over Tokyo Bay. On the P-51, the mixture control is on the lower half of the throttle quadrant. The manual bomb release is on a straight line from the pilot's shoulder past the mixture control. If the pilot grasps the bomb release palm up, there is no trouble, but if he grasps the release palm down, his arm almost invariably hits the mixture control. My misfortune was all caused by my mixture control being pushed into "Idle cut-off" accidentally by my arm when I was struggling with the bomb release.

The incidents quoted above are only a sample of the group collected by Fitts and Jones, but they illustrate several different kinds of trouble and suggest some solutions. Despite their variety and singularity, all 460 of the incidents could be classified into one of six major categories:

    1. *Substitution errors:* Confusing one control with another or failing to identify a control when it was needed. In general, most of these errors were due to (a) lack of uniformity in the placement of controls, (b) inadequate separation of controls, and (c) lack of a coding system

to help the pilot identify controls positively by the sense of touch alone.

2. *Adjustment errors:* Operating a control too slowly or too rapidly, moving a switch to the wrong position, or following the wrong sequence in operating several controls. The most common single kind of error in this category was made by turning the fuel-selector switch so that it was halfway between two tanks and leaving it in a position where fuel could flow from neither tank, or actually turning the switch to the wrong tank.

3. *Forgetting errors:* Failing to check, unlock, or use a control at the proper time.

4. *Reversal errors:* Moving a control in a direction opposite to that necessary to produce the desired result. Many such errors could be traced to the fact that controls sometimes would not move in "expected" directions.

5. *Unintentional activation:* Accidentally operating a control without being aware of it.

6. *Inability to reach:* Difficulty in reaching a control.

You should have no trouble finding incidents from your own experience to illustrate each of these problems. If you cannot recall any incidents of these kinds offhand, notice carefully the way you use everyday equipment such as your automobile, stove, power tools, or television set, and see whether you can uncover difficulties of each of the six types reported by Fitts and Jones.

Some General Principles for Selecting Controls

There are eleven basic classes of controls in common use: hand pushbuttons, foot pushbuttons, toggle switches, rocker switches, rotary switches, knobs, cranks, thumbwheels, levers, handwheels, and pedals. Each of these can be found in an almost infinite variety of shapes, sizes, and arrangements. Detailed design specifications are available for each type of control, and Figure 5–1 and Table 5–1 illustrate that sort of information. It is important to know that such information exists, so that you can find it whenever you need it. However, to give such design specifications for all the basic types of controls would involve us in much more detail than is warranted. Therefore, I shall confine my discussion of controls to more general principles.

The first and most important step in designing controls for effective human use is to pick the best control for the job. In itself, a control is neither "good" nor "bad." It is merely *appropriate* or *inappropriate*. A toggle switch is fine for turning on electric lights, but it is not a good way to apply a braking force to an automobile; a foot pedal is excellent

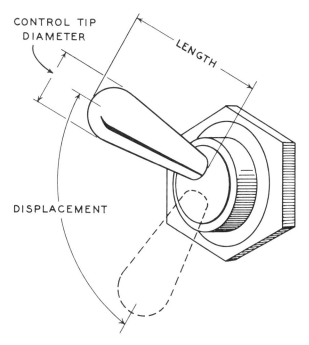

FIGURE 5–1. *Toggle switch with some critical dimensions identified.*

for controlling the brakes on an automobile, but hardly a suitable way of typing.

Defining the Job

In selecting a control for a job, the engineer needs to specify the job in some detail. He should consider the following four major points:

1. *What will the control do?* Will it be used to turn on a light,

TABLE 5–1.   *Design recommendations for toggle-switch controls.* (From Morgan et al., 25.)

LEVER-TIP DIAMETER[*]	
Minimum	⅛ in.
Maximum	1 in.
LEVER-ARM LENGTH[*]	
Minimum	½ in.
Maximum	2 in.
DISPLACEMENT[*]	
Minimum	40 deg.[†]
Maximum	120 deg.[‡]
RESISTANCE	
Minimum	10 oz.
Maximum	40 oz.
NUMBER OF POSITIONS	
Minimum	2
Maximum	3

[*] See Figure 5–1.
[†] Between adjacent positions.
[‡] Total displacement.

move a needle on a dial, turn a caterpillar tractor, elevate a hoist, or set an automatic washing machine into action?

2. *What does the task require?* Is it important that the operator make a precise setting, or will a coarse one do? How quickly does the operator have to make the control movement? What range of settings will be required by the job? How much muscular force will the operator have to exert? Will the operator be wearing restrictive clothing, such as heavy gloves, or be otherwise restrained?

3. *What information does the operator need to get from the control?* Is it important that the operator be able to identify the control by sight, or by touch alone? Will he have to distinguish this particular control from others around it? Should the operator be able to tell by sight or by touch how the control is set?

4. *What restrictions are imposed by the environment?* Are there any limitations of size or placement that are imposed by the vehicle, the enclosure, or the equipment where the control will be located? Must the control be readily associated with a display? Are there any other environmental conditions, such as darkness, vibration, or movement, that might affect the use of a particular control?

Selecting the Best Control for the Job

In the process of defining the job carefully, the designer will have done much to settle early the question of what control is best for the job. Very often, a simple consideration of the task itself will narrow the alternatives to one or two possibilities (see Table 5–2). This table does not tell the whole story, however, and some additional rules that may enter into the choice of a control are given below.

TABLE 5–2. *Recommended controls for various types of tasks.* (After Morgan et al., 25.)

FOR SMALL FORCES AND	USE
2 discrete settings	Hand pushbutton, foot pushbutton, toggle switch, or rocker switch
3 discrete settings	Finger pushbutton, toggle switch, or rotary selector switch
4 to 24 discrete settings	Bank or array of finger pushbuttons, rotary selector switch, or detented thumbwheel
25 or more discrete settings	Bank or array of finger pushbuttons
Small range of continuous settings	Knob, lever, or thumbwheel
Large range of continuous settings	Crank

FOR LARGE FORCES AND	USE
2 discrete settings	Detent lever, large hand pushbutton, or foot pushbutton
3 to 24 discrete settings	Detent lever
Small range of continuous settings	Handwheel, rotary pedal, or lever
Large range of continuous settings	Large crank

CONTROLS SHOULD MATCH THE LIMB

Although it is theoretically possible to use many different parts of the human body to activate controls, only the hands and the feet are used for this purpose. Perhaps the most important rule to observe in this connection is that none of the limbs should be overburdened. If the operator has a number of controls to use, they should be distributed among the four limbs.

Since the four limbs differ in their capabilities, controls should be selected to match these capabilities. Generally speaking, many controls of many different kinds can be assigned to the hands, but no more than two simple controls should be assigned to each foot. Since most people are right-handed, the major load should be assigned to the right hand. Finally, controls that must be adjusted rapidly and with great precision should be assigned to the hands; those requiring the application of large forces to the feet.

CONTROLS SHOULD MATCH THE TASK

Controls should mimic the movements they produce in the system. For example, a lever that moves up and down conforms naturally to the up-and-down movements of the landing gear on an aircraft and the rotation of a steering wheel in an automobile conforms naturally to the turning motions of the vehicle itself. When the movements of a control are naturally and easily associated with the movements of the display, vehicle, or component, the two are said to be *compatible*.

FUNCTIONALLY RELATED CONTROLS SHOULD BE COMBINED

When an operator uses a large number of controls, it is often advantageous to have related controls combined. For example, my automobile windshield wipers have two controls. One is a hand-operated rotary switch, the other is a foot pedal. The foot pedal sets the windshield wipers into action for as long as the pedal is partially depressed. Pressing the pedal farther sets the windshield washer into operation. After a rainstorm, passing cars often spray water from the road onto my windshield. Since my hands are occupied with steering, it is convenient and safer to use a foot control to activate the windshield wipers. There are other circumstances when it is convenient to wash and wipe the windshield while the car is in motion. Since these are functionally related operations, they are sensibly combined.

The principal advantages of combined controls are that they reduce the number of movements required to operate a number of controls, they help the operator use several controls at the same time or in sequence, and they save space. In combining controls, however, it is important not to violate other human-engineering principles, such as optimum *control-display ratios* and *natural movement relationships*, which will be discussed later in this chapter.

CONTROLS SHOULD BE EASILY IDENTIFIED

Whenever several or many controls are to be used on the same panel or in the same area, they should be maximally distinguishable from one another. This basic problem is usually referred to as the problem of *control coding*.

Factors in the Design of Controls

A number of design factors keep cropping up in connection with many types of controls. Perhaps the most important of these are *control-display ratios, direction-of-movement relationships,* and *methods of coding controls.*

Control-Display Ratios

A control-display-ratio problem exists whenever a control is used to change the position of a movable element in a display and both the control and display are continuously adjustable. Figure 5-2 shows a tuning knob used to position the needle on the frequency scale of a

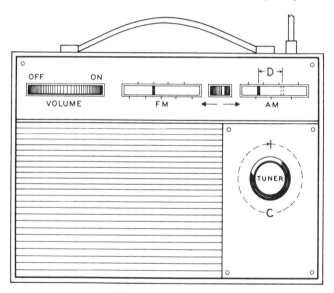

FIGURE 5-2. *The control-display (C/D) ratio on this portable radio is defined as the number of rotations of the tuning knob needed to make the needle on the scale move a specified distance.*

radio. The control-display (C/D) ratio is defined as the number of rotations (C in the figure) of the tuning knob per unit of linear distance (D in the figure) the needle travels on the scale. Although Figure 5-2 shows a particular combination of control and display, the same problem occurs with several different kinds of controls (levers, cranks, or handwheels) and displays (linear-vertical, linear-horizontal, circular, or spots on cathode-ray tubes that move in two dimensions). Because the linkage between a control and a moving display element is often some sort of a gearing arrangement, the C/D ratio is occasionally referred to as a *gear ratio*.

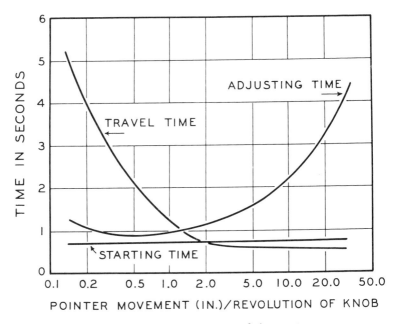

FIGURE 5–3. *The time required for setting an indicator with different control-display ratios. Although the numerical values can change, the shapes of these curves are typical of the results obtained in studies of C/D ratios.* (Based on data from Jenkins and Connor, 17.)

CONTROL MOVEMENTS AS A FUNCTION OF THE C/D RATIO

Figure 5–3 shows the kind of data that typically come out of studies on C/D ratios. Three kinds of time are involved. First is the *normal reaction time*, the time required for the hand or the foot to reach the control and start moving it once the operator has decided to make the movement. Reaction time is independent of the gear ratio, and appears as a flat line in Figure 5–3. The second is the time required for a *gross adjustment,* to move the needle to approximately the correct setting. This time is sometimes referred to as *slewing time, travel time,* or *primary-movement time.* As you can see, gross-adjustment time is markedly dependent on the C/D ratio. If the needle or display element moves only a small distance for each revolution of the knob, the operator must usually make many revolutions to get in the vicinity of the correct setting. On the other hand, if the display element moves a substantial distance for each revolution of the knob, the gross-adjustment time is short.

The third time is that for making *fine adjustments,* the final precise positioning of the display element. This time is sometimes called the *adjusting-movement time,* or the *secondary-movement time.* For fine adjustments, the time involved is exactly the reverse of that for gross adjustments. If the display element moves only a small distance for each revolution of the knob, it is easy to set the display element precisely. If the needle makes large swings, the operator finds it difficult to make precise settings, because he frequently overshoots the mark and has to keep making corrective movements.

The best C/D ratio is one that minimizes the sum of these three times. In the example shown in Figure 5–3, the ratio is about 1.2 inches of pointer movement per revolution of the control knob.

SELECTING OPTIMUM C/D RATIOS

The C/D ratio has a substantial influence on the efficiency of the operator using a control. In the study from which the data in Figure 5–3 were taken, Jenkins and Connor studied several other design variables—knob diameter, knobs versus cranks, and backlash. But they report that no other design factor in their experiment was so important as the C/D ratio.

Nonetheless, it is almost impossible at the present time to give a satisfactory set of summary recommendations about the optimum C/D ratio. Too many factors affect it—display size, the allowable tolerance in making the settings, viewing distance, time delays in the system, and the size of the control element. If the designer has a control-display problem exactly like one that has already been tested experimentally, he is safe in using the C/D ratio found in that study. Otherwise, about the best we can say is that the C/D ratio is important and that it should be determined experimentally for each situation.

Direction-of-Movement Relationships and Operator Expectations

In their study of errors made in using aircraft controls, Fitts and Jones (11) found that one of the major categories of error was *reversal errors,* errors made by moving the control in the wrong direction. At first glance, one might suppose that errors of this kind are caused by the operator's lack of training. Further analysis, however, reveals that the situation is not so simple as that. The fact of the matter is that most people *expect* controls to move in certain ways. In some cases, these expectancies are so universal that they have been termed *population stereotypes.*

When controls, and control-display arrangements conform to population stereotypes, we find in general that:

1. Reaction time, or decision time, is shorter.

2. The first control movement the operator makes is more likely to be correct.

3. The operator can use the control faster and make adjustments with greater precision.

4. The operator can learn to use the control (or control-display combination) much faster.

People are remarkably adaptive and can often learn to compensate for deficiencies in equipment design. It is not surprising, therefore, to find that operators can learn to use controls that do not move in expected directions. The danger, however, is that when operators are under stress or anxiety, these learned habits often break down—with the result that the operator reverts to more natural (though incorrect) movements. The experimental evidence on this point is so strong that we may adopt it as a general principle: We should not ask an operator to make unnatural movements, especially since it is so easy to design equipment properly in the first place.

We do not know as much about direction-of-movement relationships as we should like, but some of the more dependable findings are summarized below.

CONTROL MOVEMENTS FOR VARIOUS SYSTEM RESPONSES

Controls are sometimes used to produce a change in a system or in a component of the system. For example, we may flip a toggle switch to start a motor, push a lever to elevate a hoist, or turn a knob to increase the rate of flow of a liquid. The system response may, or may not, be immediately displayed to the operator. Some dependable direction-of-motion relationships for use under these conditions are summarized in Figure 5–4.

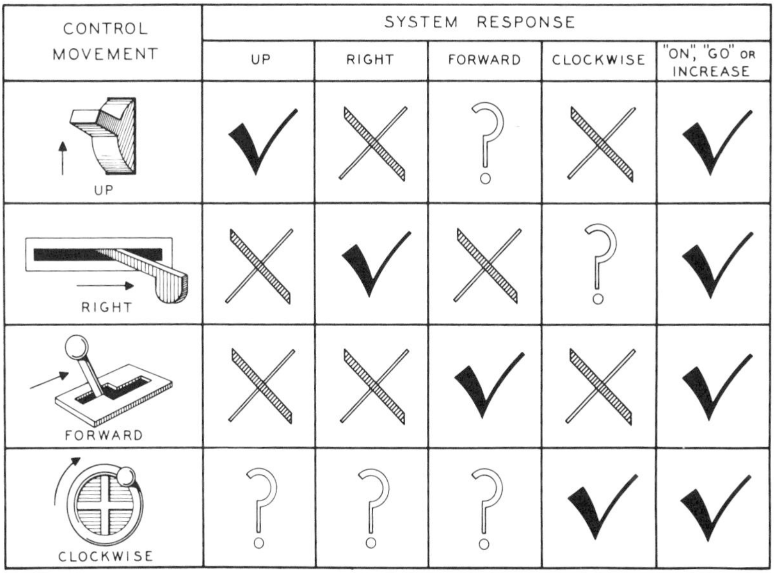

CONTROL MOVEMENT	SYSTEM RESPONSE				
	UP	RIGHT	FORWARD	CLOCKWISE	"ON", "GO" OR INCREASE
UP	✓	✗	?	✗	✓
RIGHT	✗	✓	✗	?	✓
FORWARD	✗	✗	✓	✗	✓
CLOCKWISE	?	?	?	✓	✓

FIGURE 5–4. *Some direction-of-movement relationships for various system responses.* (After Morgan et al., 25.)

The recommendations given in Figure 5–4 hold for related types of controls. For example, the movement relationships for toggle switches are the same as those for levers. In addition, movement relationships for knobs, cranks, and wheels are essentially identical. Check marks in the figure show those relationships that are recommended; X's show those relationships that are definitely not recommended; and question marks show those relationships that may or may not be acceptable, depending on circumstances.

PROBLEMS OF STANDARDIZATION

It is not hard to find examples in which these movement relationships are violated; Figure 5–5 shows only two of many that could be offered. This figure is particularly appropriate because it shows a simple kind of control—a toggle switch—in which the expected movement relationships are obvious. Almost as important is the fact that all four of these toggle switches were found on standard equipment in our own laboratories at Johns Hopkins—by which I mean that I did not have to search very far to locate some examples. In this illustration, toggle switches flip in all four directions—up, down, right, and left—simply to turn something *on.*

FIGURE 5–5. *Four toggle switches on items of standard equipment.*

Although this kind of inconsistency may not be disastrous within the confines of an academic institution, it is not difficult to find cases in which such problems are serious. In the Berlin Airlift of 1948 and 1949, all the needs—food, fuel, clothing, medicine, books, machinery, and the thousand and one other items that a modern city needs to survive—of approximately 3,000,000 people had to be supplied by air. The airlift was carried out by the United States First Airlift Task Force and the British 46th Group. Almost all of the aircraft used by the U.S. Task Force were one type of four-engine plane, widely used for both commercial and military transport, made by a single company. Yet one of the most frequent complaints by pilots concerned the lack of standardization among the instruments and controls in these aircraft. A pilot often flew three different aircraft in one flight period. After having learned one instrument and control arrangement on his first flight, the pilot had to forget it and immediately learn another for his very next flight. I think you will agree that inconsistencies in control arrangements are no longer trivial considerations. Indeed, one serious accident was conclusively traced to lack of standardization in the way fuel-selector controls operated in different models of the same aircraft.

An interesting problem of population stereotypes and standardization is the labeling of pushbuttons for an electric range. In the top half of Figure 5–6 are six pushbuttons that control the cooking speed

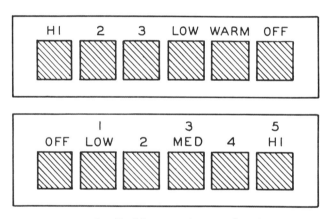

FIGURE 5–6. *Pushbuttons for an electric stove as the manufacturer originally designed them (above), and the stereotypes which housewives had about these pushbuttons (below). (After Javitz, 16.)*

of a single burner on an electric range. The markings are as the manufacturer originally designed them.

The consulting firm of Dunlap and Associates studied this arrangement of pushbuttons and discovered some interesting stereotypes. In the first place, housewives typically expect the "Off" button to be on the far left. Moreover, they expect increasing heat to be associated with buttons from left to right. Finally, they expect the button labeled "3" to be associated with more heat than the button labeled "2." Similarly, they expect the button labeled "Warm" to produce more heat than the one labeled "Low." We may speculate that the manufacturer designed the labels from the back, since he would associate "3" with more *resistance* (but less heat) than "2." In any event, the lower half of Figure 5–6 shows the set of pushbuttons relabeled to conform to the housewives' stereotypes.

CONTROLS AND DISPLAYS IN THE SAME PLANE

One of the most important recommendations concerning display-control arrangements is that the control and the display should be in the same plane. When this condition is satisfied, you have some of the strongest and most dependable direction-of-movement stereotypes (see Fig. 5–7). Insofar as possible, display-control relationships should be picked from one of those shown in Figure 5–7. It is especially important to avoid using a moving-dial indicator with a fixed mark, if at all possible. (See the discussion of these indicators on pp. 44–47.) In addition, rotary controls should not be placed above any display or to the left of linear vertical displays.

CONTROLS AND DISPLAYS IN DIFFERENT PLANES

Tests have been made of a great many combinations of controls and displays mounted in different planes. The list of combinations that do *not* yield clear-cut stereotypes is long, and most have been illustrated in the article by Loveless (22). Figure 5–8, however, shows some of the stereotypes that are most dependable and do work. They should be used in those cases when the control and the display cannot be mounted in the same plane.

Control Coding

In their study of aircraft controls, Fitts and Jones found that one of the most frequent kinds of errors was that in which a pilot mistook one control for another. That this same kind of trouble can be found in other situations is amply demonstrated in a survey made by Bilinski (2). Bilinski observed maintenance men using consoles of various types and counted the number of errors they made in using the controls on these consoles. One of his major findings was that the proportion of

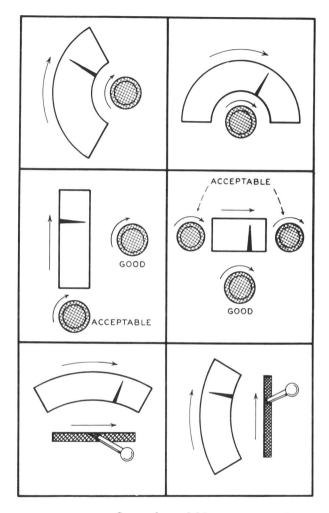

FIGURE 5–7. *Some dependable stereotypes for controls and displays mounted in the same plane.* (Based on data from Loveless, 22.)

errors increased markedly as the number of knobs on the console increased.

One way of reducing errors of this type is to code the controls so that they are easier to identify and less likely to be confused. Four methods of control coding are in common use: shape, size, color, and labeling.

SHAPE CODING

Coding controls by varying their shapes is an especially effective way of making them distinctive. A great many different shapes can be constructed, and shape coding is effective both visually and tactually, that is, the difference can be both seen and felt. Two general rules are often followed in shape coding: (1) the shape of a control should suggest its purpose, and (2) the shape should be distinguishable not only

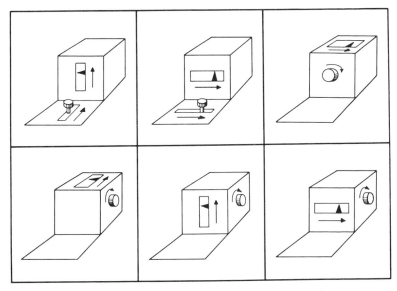

FIGURE 5–8. *Some dependable stereotypes for controls and displays mounted in different planes.* (Based on data from Loveless, 22.)

with the naked hand, but also with gloves. As a result of careful work on many different kinds of shape-coded controls, we have available several sets of shapes that can be easily discriminated by both naked and gloved hands. The set illustrated in Figure 5–9 is currently being used in the Air Force.

SIZE CODING

Size coding is not so effective as shape coding, because the number of different sizes that can be correctly discriminated by touch alone is very small. In fact, if the operator must be able to decide whether he is grasping the correct control without comparing it with the other controls adjacent to it then there are only three sizes that can be used dependably: a small, a medium, and a large control. Each of these should be at least 20 per cent larger than the next smaller one.

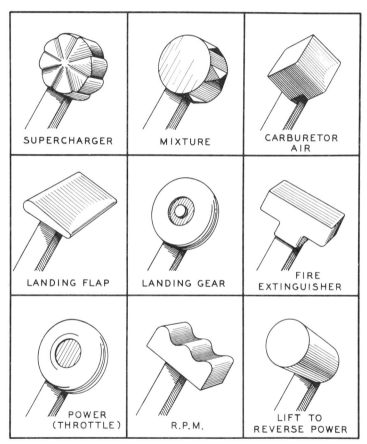

FIGURE 5–9.   *Some shape-coded controls for use in the Air Force.* (After Morgan et al., 25.)

CODING WITH LABELS

Labeling is another highly effective method of coding controls, largely because the number of alternatives is almost unlimited. The chief requirements for coding in this way are adequate space and lighting. Labels should be highly legible; they should be placed on the control or close to it; they should make use of common words or common abbreviations; and they should tell what is being controlled.

COLOR CODING

Color coding should generally not be used alone, but should be combined with other methods of coding, such as size or shape. Color coding is effective only when there is adequate illumination that does not distort the colors. Although the eye can distinguish many different colors, only five can be depended upon for control coding: red, orange, yellow, green, and blue.

The Arrangement of Controls and Displays

The ease and accuracy of control operation interacts with the general work environment. The location of the control in the work environment, the relation of particular controls to one another, and the location of controls with respect to their associated displays—all these are important considerations as well.

Some General Rules for Control Placement

The following rules are primarily concerned with the location of controls in the workplace and in their relation to the operator. These rules are not specific to any particular kind of control; they supplement all the rules of good control design that have been discussed so far.

STANDARDIZE

Perhaps the most important rule for the design of machine systems is that the arrangement of controls and displays be standardized. The same groupings of controls and displays should be used in all similar models of the equipment. Moreover, all controls that look alike should behave alike. If the rule of standardization cannot be followed for some reason, the exceptions to it should be made obvious to the operator.

TAKE SPECIAL PRECAUTIONS WITH EMERGENCY CONTROLS

Because of their importance, emergency controls require special attention. First, emergency controls should be clearly distinguished from all others by being physically separated from them. Next, emergency controls should be located where they can be easily reached by the operator, no matter what his momentary position might be. They should be placed within 30 degrees of the operator's normal line of sight and should be distinctively coded so that they will not be confused with other controls. Finally, emergency controls should be recessed, covered with guards, shielded, or otherwise protected so that they cannot be inadvertently operated.

ARRANGE CONTROLS IN SEQUENCE

When an operator must use a number of controls in a fixed or definite sequence, the controls should be arranged so that the operator's hand or foot moves in a smooth, continuous movement (for example, left to right, or through an arc) in operating them.

PROVIDE RESTS OR SUPPORTS FOR THE OPERATOR

When controls must be operated with great force or precision, give the operator proper support. If he must exert a force of more than 5 pounds on a hand control, give him a backrest against which he can push or a footrest to help him in pulling. Supports for the arm, the heel of the hand, the wrist, or the foot are especially important if a control must be operated smoothly and with precision.

GIVE THE OPERATOR ROOM TO MOVE

When the operator must be on duty for a long time, or when he must operate controls requiring the application of large forces, it is important that he have room to stretch, to shift his position from time to time, and to move his arms, hands, and feet. Controls should therefore be placed where they can allow the operator to be reasonably mobile.

The Location of Controls and Displays

There are two general methods used for grouping controls and displays. Although both are effective, the basic philosophies underlying each are quite different.

The first method of grouping is *functional*. Controls and displays that are identical in function, that are used together, or that relate to some one part of a system are grouped together. In an aircraft, for example, all the controls having to do with the functioning of the engines (throttles, carburetor-air-mixture controls, and so on) are together.

Those having to do with flight attitude are grouped separately. The other method of grouping is *sequential*. Here controls and displays are arranged in the order in which they would normally be used. The controls and displays on the graphic control panel in Figure 2–5 are of this type—they are arranged in the order in which the various operations are carried out in the oil refinery.

CONTROL-DISPLAY ARRANGEMENTS IN STOVES

To illustrate the importance of control-display arrangements in determining operator performance, we can turn to a simple experiment

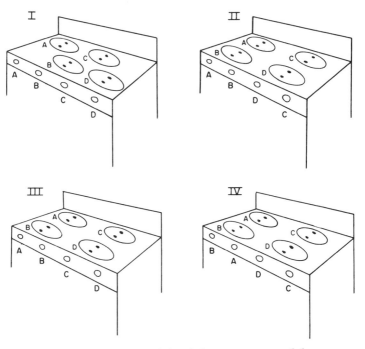

FIGURE 5–10. *Models of four stoves tested by Chapanis and Lindenbaum (8).*

by Chapanis and Lindenbaum (8). Various gas and electric kitchen stoves have several different linkages between the controls and the burners. Figure 5–10 shows four that are representative of stoves being currently manufactured, although the design identified as "I" is uncommon. These four arrangements do not exhaust all the possibilities, since there is at least one other control-burner linkage on the market.

The purpose of the experiment was straightforward. Subjects were tested to discover how quickly and how accurately they could associate the control on the front panel with the burner on the top surface. Fifteen different subjects (sixty in all) were tested on each stove, and each subject was tested for eighty consecutive trials. When a light appeared near the center of one of the burners, the subject had to respond as quickly as possible by pushing the correct control.

The results of the experiment show that the rank ordering of the four stoves from best to poorest is in the order in which they are numbered in Figure 5–10. Out of a total of 1,200 trials made on each stove, there were no errors made with "I," 76 with "II," 116 with "III," and 129 with "IV." The average response times agree with the error data: the arrangement on which subjects made no errors gave the shortest average response time, the one on which the subjects made the most errors gave the longest average response time. It is clear that control-display arrangements have an important effect on performance.

SOME GENERAL PRINCIPLES OF CONTROL-DISPLAY ARRANGEMENTS

It is difficult to devise a set of general rules to cover *all* the possible kinds of control-display arrangements that designers or inventors dream up. At the moment, for example, there is no simple rule to cover the findings of the stove experiment described above. Nonetheless, some rules seem to be so general and dependable that they could be called principles. These are:

1. Displays and controls that are to be used in a fixed order should be arranged in sequence (a) from left to right, (b) from top to bottom, or (c) in rows from top to bottom, and from left to right within the rows.

2. When a number of displays and controls are each associated with a group of similar components, the arrangement of the controls and displays should correspond with the arrangement of the components. (For example, in a four-engine aircraft, the four throttle controls, RPM indicators, and mixture controls, should be arranged from left to right in the same order as the engines themselves.)

3. Controls associated with specific displays should be located so that the operator's hand does not prevent him from seeing the display. When a number of associated controls and displays appear on a panel, (a) put each control directly below its corresponding display or (b)

group all the displays above and all the controls below, but arrange the controls and the displays in exactly the same order (see Fig. 5–11).

4. If concentric, or ganged, knobs are used to control a set of displays (see Fig. 5–12), the uppermost (smallest) knob should operate

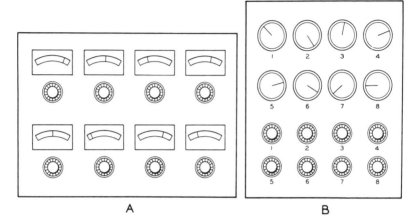

A   B

FIGURE 5–11. *Two preferred ways of grouping controls and their associated displays.* (After Morgan et al., 25.)

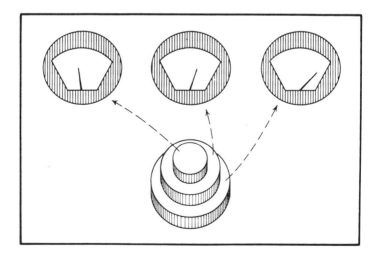

FIGURE 5–12. *When concentric knobs are used to control several displays, the linkages should be as shown here.* (After Morgan et al., 25.)

the farthest-left display, and the largest (lowermost) knob the farthest-right display.

Summary

This chapter has been concerned with the design of controls, the mechanisms by which man communicates instructions and information to machines. The chapter summarizes a classic study of controls that is interesting because of its method, the so-called *critical-incident technique,* and because of its finding that poorly designed controls invite their operators to make errors. These errors fall into six principal types. The rest of the chapter is essentially concerned with ways of designing controls to avoid these errors. First, one has to select the correct control for the job, and we found that there are a number of rules to help us here. The chapter then discusses some general design principles, control-display ratios, direction-of-movement relationships, and control coding, and concludes with some rules for arranging controls and displays.

The next chapter takes a look backward and one forward, to tell us where we could and should go from here.

chapter
six

Perspectives
and Postscript

In writing any book, an author has to make a choice: Should he try to survey the whole field superficially or should he concentrate on a few parts of it, elaborating these in some detail while ignoring the other parts? The first alternative sacrifices depth for breadth; the latter does the reverse.

In writing this book, I chose the second alternative. A few topics in engineering psychology have been deliberately picked out of the whole field and discussed in moderate detail. As a result, it is possible that you might end up with some incorrect ideas of what the field of human engineering is really about. One purpose of this chapter is to fill in some of the gaps—at least to the extent of identifying what they are.

Other Topics in Engineering Psychology

It's difficult to say precisely what is and what is not important for an engineering psychologist to know. Part of this difficulty lies in the fact that man-machine problems occur in almost infinite variety. In addition, the range of these problems is increasing rather than contracting. Our engineers are busy designing new, complex machines, not only for our everyday lives, but for use in hostile and exotic environments where man was never supposed to live—from the abysses of the oceans to the infinite voids of outer space. For reasons such as these, man-machine problems seem to be multiplying faster than we can do research on them. Nonetheless, most engineering psychologists, and human factors engineers, would probably agree that they need to know certain other information if they are to be competent in their work.

Broadly speaking, these data fall into two main groups: that of *content* and that of *method.*

Some Content Areas of Engineering Psychology

EXPERIMENTAL PSYCHOLOGY

This book is primarily machine oriented. Visual displays, for example, are discussed entirely from the point of view of the displays and how they should be designed. There is nothing about the eye itself or what conditions make it a more effective sensing device. Chapter 4 treats auditory communication systems in the same way. There is much discussion there about the design of systems, of components, and of languages, but nothing about the ear.

But the engineering psychologist needs to know the whole content of normal human experimental psychology as well. Information about the sensitivity of the eye is important for knowing how to construct effective visual signaling systems. Basic data on the sensitivity of the ear is used in selecting and designing auditory signals for sonar, radio-range signals, sirens, and scores of other signals. Knowing about the normal human memory span is helpful in deciding about numeral and letter codes for such things as telephones. Man's ability to learn interacts with the design of everything he uses. The ways in which people work, become tired, and sleep turn out to be of vital importance in designing schedules for isolated work stations in the arctic and deep space.

PRINTED MATERIALS

One of the most important forms of visual communication is the printed symbol. Much material of great importance to the engineering psychologist is available on this topic. It starts with the basic design of isolated numerals and letters, ranges through the selection of print styles for easy legibility and the choice of special symbols for charts and maps, and ends with the design of tables, graphs, nomographs, and other forms of printed display. Books have been written about the legibility of print alone. Problems involving printed materials and their use are ubiquitous and most engineering psychologists are certain to become involved with them at one time or another.

CATHODE-RAY TUBES

So much information is now relayed to man indirectly, by way of radar and related kinds of systems, that it is important to know about the problems of cathode-ray tubes. Some of these problems are the size of the display, its brightness, the type of phosphor used, the contrast between targets and their backgrounds, clutter, the form in which information is displayed, and ways in which information can be coded.

TONAL SIGNALING SYSTEMS

A large class of auditory display systems makes use of auditory signals other than speech. Horns, sirens, radio-range signals, buzzers, and sonar are some examples. There is a large body of information available on the selection of signals for specific listening situations, on the processing of these signals for best interpretability, and on the best intensities for listening.

COMMUNICATION SYSTEMS FOR SENSES OTHER THAN VISION AND HEARING

Although vision and hearing are the most important sense channels man has for receiving information, we must not ignore his other senses. The sense of touch, for example, is used routinely by the blind for reading and for sensing the world around them. It is also used by machine operators for distinguishing controls and acquiring information when they cannot use their eyes and ears.

The vibratory sense is another important medium of communication. With one vibratory signaling system (14), subjects have been able to receive up to 38 words per minute! This rate surpasses good performance with auditory Morse code by a substantial margin. Another vibratory signaling system has been constructed to provide auxiliary flight information to pilots (1). Such applications are unusual, but they illustrate that the so-called lower senses can be of considerable importance in certain types of man-machine systems.

CLOSED-LOOP TRACKING SYSTEMS

A closed-loop tracking system is a man-machine system containing a display that usually transmits constantly changing information to the operator. The operator senses this information, ordinarily through his eyes or ears, and moves a control or controls accordingly. The operator's control produces some action in the machine and some resultant change in the system. In a closed-loop system, information about the performance of the system is fed back into the display, so that the operator sees a combination of information about the system input and the system output.

Driving an automobile is a familiar illustration of a closed-loop tracking system. The system input is the panorama of the road, the traffic, and the outline of the driver's own automobile. The controls are the steering wheel, accelerator, and brake, and they act upon the automobile to produce the movements of the automobile. Other examples of closed-loop systems are flying an airplane, diving a submarine, steering a ship, and operating a power shovel.

Good human engineering practice is required in the design of every part of such closed-loop systems. Even more important, there is a considerable body of knowledge about the design parameters of such systems, on such things as transmission lags in the system, on aiding, on providing derivative information on displays, and on time constants, all of which form a significant part of the content of engineering psychology.

THE ARRANGEMENT OF GROUPS OF MEN AND EQUIPMENT

Not all man-machine systems have only one man working with one machine. Factors contributing to the design of multiple-crew stations, on the layouts of equipment in such stations, and on the factors that make for compatibility among the men in such systems could easily form at least a chapter in a comprehensive textbook.

DESIGN FOR EASE OF MAINTENANCE

As more and more systems become automated, human engineering problems shift from the man as an operator of the equipment to man as a maintainer of the equipment. Some feeling for the importance of this problem may be conveyed by the fact that the Consumer Service Division of the Detroit Edison Company repairs some 600,000 appliances in a typical year (see also p. 25). Much of the cost of servicing and maintaining equipment is caused by time wasted in locating and getting to the defective part. In an automobile I once owned, the service man reported that he had to deactivate and disassemble the air conditioning equipment in order to get to the spark plugs!

Ease of maintenance can help greatly in reducing the costs of repairs and in reducing the amount of time that equipment is out of service. But easy maintenance does not just happen. It has to be designed into the equipment by providing adequate doors and accesses, by building in test points and other fault-finding aids, by providing necessary tools and auxiliary equipment, and by providing clear and comprehensive maintenance manuals. The design recommendations about ease of maintenance are so numerous that they could easily fill a couple of chapters.

ENVIRONMENTAL EFFECTS

A man-machine system does not exist in isolation. It exists in an environment of some sort. The character of this environment influences man's efficiency and performance, and the engineering psychologist is often vitally concerned with these factors. Among the important environmental influences are movement, temperature, humidity, ventilation, lighting, and noise. Among the less familiar ones are vibration, noxious gases, and contaminants. In space-exploration systems, we also have to be concerned with the effects of increased acceleration, weightlessness, anoxia caused by reduced oxygen at high altitudes, radiation, and the effects of reduced barometric pressures on the body. Environmental effects could make another chapter of a more complete treatise on engineering psychology.

Methodology

It would be ideal if the engineering psychologist could turn to handbooks of human data, or to textbooks of psychology, physiology, and anthropology to find the information he needs, much as an engineer can turn to the *Handbook of Chemistry and Physics*, the *Radio Engineer's Handbook*, or any of a dozen others. Although a few books try to present human data in this way, the best of them falls short of providing even a substantial fraction of the kinds of information the engineering psychologist needs. In lieu of immediate textbook help, the engineering psychologist must spend a considerable amount of time "trying things out." In some industries and laboratories, experimentation of one kind or another may take up the major part of the engineering psychologist's working time. He may perform little exploratory experiments, "quick and dirty experiments," as they are often called; occasionally he may conduct surveys of one kind or another; at still other times he may engage in full-fledged experiments with the rigor and sophistication of the best experimentation in this area. So important is this aspect of the engineering psychologist's work that the study of methodology is a vital part of his education. It is important for two reasons: (a) experiments on people are more complex than conventional kinds of experiments on physical systems, and (b) the kinds of experimental techniques that the psychologist typically learns in his undergraduate course in experimental psychology are too narrow and specialized to be of much practical value.

DIFFICULTIES OF HUMAN EXPERIMENTATION

When you do a chemical experiment, you can reach up onto your shelf for a *reagent* and look at the label to see what you have. The label may identify the reagent by name, tell you its purity, and give you its chemical formula. In addition, you can be pretty sure that it will be the same this afternoon as it is this morning and that it will be the same tomorrow as it is today. You can say anything you want to it, and it will still be what the label says.

In contrast, when you reach out into the corridor for a human reagent, you do not know what you have. At best, you have a little information about the past history of your human reagent, some rough idea about the limits of its performance, and only a vague notion about its stability. You know for sure that it will not be the same this afternoon as it is this morning and that it will definitely change overnight. You can be certain that the reactions of your subject will be markedly determined by what you say, for here is a reagent that thinks and has attitudes and emotions. Finally, your human reagent is a mechanism that may try to deceive or outguess you in your attempts to find out what makes him function—an effort in which, unfortunately, he is sometimes successful. You need no further elaboration to see that experiments on people are much more complicated than experiments on simple chemical, physical, or mechanical systems.

Psychologists do not have infallible methods for dealing with these difficulties, but they have been in the business long enough to have discovered many things that work and many that won't. These methods have to be learned and learned well to avoid reaching unwarranted and downright false conclusions of the types that are often drawn from poorly designed human experiments.

VARIETIES OF METHODS IN ENGINEERING PSYCHOLOGY

The student who takes a laboratory course in experimental psychology typically learns about experimentation of the kind that is usually conducted in university laboratories. If this is the usual course, it is also likely to concentrate heavily on experiments with white rats using Skinner boxes or mazes. Although such learning is useful and contributes materially to the education of the engineering psychologist, there is a much greater variety of techniques available (4). The engineering psychologist relies heavily on *psychophysical* methods for obtaining useful data on sensory capacities. He uses *articulation-test methods* for measuring the effectiveness of speech communication devices and systems. The *critical-incident technique* is extremely valuable (pp. 93–98) for locating serious trouble spots and difficulties in man-machine systems. He often uses certain methods of direct observation borrowed from industrial engineering: activity sampling procedures, process analysis, and micromotion methods. He may also find that the best way to attack certain problems is by studying accidents and near accidents. These methods are not likely to be found in usual courses, but they are essential to the education of the engineering psychologist. If he is not well versed in methods, he will not be able to conduct studies of his own; even more important, he will be unable to evaluate properly studies by other people.

Engineering Psychology in Depth

I've tried to make this book readable and understandable. Many of the illustrations are deliberately picked from ordinary devices and everyday implements like radios, room heaters, and automobiles. The recommendations and principles are worded as simply as possible so that you can see the kinds of things that engineering psychologists try to do.

This approach, unfortunately, might give you the impression that there isn't very much more to engineering psychology than applying some simple rules or following your own common sense. If you get into the field, however, you will find that it is quite a deep subject. The really interesting problems are far more complicated than any that have been described here. Moreover, there are no simple answers to be found ready-made in books of rules, handbooks, or guides. Even "common sense" provides but shifty and dangerous ground on which to make intelligent design decisions.

It is easy to find examples of equipment that is poorly adapted to human users because it was designed on the basis of intuition, common sense, or someone's rules of logic. One difficulty with such subjective standards is that they are just that—subjective. Investigation usually reveals that people don't agree. Take, for example, the three stoves labeled "II," "III," and "IV" in Figure 5–10. Show each of these to a large group of engineers and designers and ask them which arrangement is best, which is second best, and which is poorest. The disparity of opinions you are certain to get is most instructive. Moreover, if you ask each person why he has ranked the arrangements as he has, he will almost certainly give you what appear to be sensible and logical reasons to support his point of view. But if engineers or designers cannot agree on such a simple thing as this, how is one to know how best to design something? The correct answer, of course, comes from experiments, from examining how people behave—not from what someone thinks.

In some ways, engineers are the worst people in the world to design equipment. True, they are among the most intelligent of all occupational groups, they are thoroughly at home with numbers and with mathematics, and they are conversant with mechanisms of all sorts. But the average person is not an engineer. The man or woman who uses a telephone, drives a car, or operates any of a dozen complicated pieces of modern machinery is just an ordinary citizen, a representative picked at random from the broad cross-section of humanity. He may come in any combination of the sizes, shapes, intellects, and personalities that characterize the human species. The good designer must expect such users, anticipate their needs, and outguess their shortcomings. His is no easy job, a job for which many engineers and systems designers are poorly trained.

One can also find illustrations of principles that seem to disagree with common sense. Take this example: Imagine that someone is trying to listen for a small change in the intensity of a signal in a quiet environment. The signal comes over an amplifying system, and the listener has control over the volume. If he turns the amplitude knob up, he increases the loudness of the signal and the awaited change in the signal by equal proportions. If he turns the amplitude down, he decreases the loudness of the signal and the awaited change in the signal by equal proportions. Should he turn the loudness up or down to get the best listening conditions? To take a specific set of numbers, is it easier to hear the difference between 10 and 11 db or the difference between 80 and 81 db—or doesn't it make any difference what the starting loudness is? What do you think?

The answer is that the listener has a much better chance of hearing a change in the intensity of a signal if he turns the volume up so that the signal is very loud. It's much easier to hear the difference between 80 and 81 db than between 10 and 11 db, even though the percentage of change is much smaller. This answer surprises many people because it doesn't seem reasonable. Indeed, many people can't believe the answer even when they hear it. The reason for this unusual state of affairs is a rather technical one involving some interesting psychophysical properties of the ear. If you want to know the details, consult Morgan et al. (25), pp. 151–153.

This is only one of many examples which could have been chosen to illustrate the point that in the business of making things fit people, common sense is not a trustworthy criterion. The answers are sometimes strange and unexpected. A good engineering psychologist learns, above all, to doubt. To doubt what others say, to doubt what looks reasonable, to doubt what he himself thinks, and even to look hard and critically at what comes out of some scientific experiments.

Human factors problems are far more complicated and perplexing than any we've talked about here. Consider the problem of what astronauts can and should do when they first land on the moon. The uncertainties are so great, the unknowns so many, that scientists can only proceed cautiously in formulating possible principles. Each trip into deep space gives us new information, valuable data, and helpful insights by means of which we progressively refine our tentative answers. Sometimes, factors that we thought important become increasingly unimportant. At other times factors that we hadn't considered at all turn out to be crucial. And so by simulation, by experiment, by past experience, and by guessing, we advance into the unknown areas of man-machine relationships.

Reading this book will not qualify you as a full-fledged engineering psychologist. But I hope that it will have excited your interest in this field and that it will stimulate you to read further and perhaps do some work in it. The really exciting problems in engineering psychology are still out there—waiting to be solved.

references

1. Ballard, J. W., and Hessinger, R. W.   Human-engineered electro-mechanical tactual sensory control system. *Electrical Manufacturing*, 1954, *54* (4), 118–121.

2. Bilinski, R.   Instrument design for the elimination of errors in use. *Electrical Manufacturing*, 1958, *62* (3), 110–112.

3. Cadwalader, Mary H.   Air mystery is solved. *Life*, 1957, *42* (17), 151–152 et passim.

4. Chapanis, A.   *Research techniques in human engineering.* Baltimore, Md.: Johns Hopkins Press, 1959.

5. Chapanis, A.   Human engineering. Chap. 19, pp. 534–582, in Flagle, C. D., Huggins, W. H., and Roy, R. H. (Eds.), *Operations research and systems engineering.* Baltimore, Md.: Johns Hopkins Press, 1960.

6. Chapanis, A., Garner, W. R., and Morgan, C. T.   *Applied experimental psychology.* New York: Wiley, 1949.

7. Chapanis, A., and Leyzorek, M.   Accuracy of visual interpolation between scale markers as a function of the number assigned to the scale interval. *J. exp. Psychol.*, 1950, *40*, 655–667.

8. Chapanis, A., and Lindenbaum, L. E.   A reaction time study of four control-display linkages. *Hum. Factors*, 1959, *1* (4), 1–7.

9. Crossman, E. R. F. W.   *Automation and skill.* London: Her Majesty's Stationery Office, 1960.

10. Egan, J. P., Carterette, E. C., and Thwing, E. J.   Some factors affecting multi-channel listening. *J. Acoust. Soc. Amer.*, 1954, *26*, 774–782.

11. Fitts, P. M., and Jones, R. E.   Analysis of factors contributing to 460 "pilot-error" experiences in operating aircraft controls. Paper 8, pp. 332–358, in Sinaiko, H. W. (Ed.), *Selected papers on human factors in the design and use of control systems.* New York: Dover Publications, 1961.

12. Fleming, J. G.   Improve power-plant instrumentation by applying human-engineering data. *Power*, 1954, *98* (1), 86–89 et passim.

13. *FSF/FAA Project SCAN Final Report.* Flight Safety Foundation, Inc. (468 Park Avenue South, New York 16, New York), 31 August 1962. 94 pp.

14. Geldard, F. A. Adventures in tactile literacy. *Amer. Psychologist,* 1957, *12,* 115–124.

15. Hecht, S., Ross, S., and Mueller, C. G. The visibility of lines and squares at high brightnesses. *J. Opt. Soc. Amer.,* 1947, *37,* 500–507.

16. Javitz, A. E. Introduction to human engineering in product design. *Electrical Manufacturing,* 1952, *49* (3), 90–95 et passim.

17. Jenkins, W. L., and Connor, M. B. Some design factors in making settings on a linear scale. *J. appl. Psychol.,* 1949, *33,* 395–409.

18. Judd, D. B., and Wyszecki, G. *Color in business, science, and industry.* New York: Wiley, 1963.

19. Licklider, J. C. R. Effects of amplitude distortion upon the intelligibility of speech. *J. Acoust. Soc. Amer.,* 1946, *18,* 429–434.

20. Licklider, J. C. R., Bindra, D., and Pollack, I. The intelligibility of rectangular speech-waves. *Amer. J. Psychol.,* 1948, *61,* 1–20.

21. Licklider, J. C. R., and Miller, G. A. The perception of speech. Chap. 26, pp. 1040–1074, in Stevens, S. S. (Ed.), *Handbook of experimental psychology.* New York: Wiley, 1951.

22. Loveless, N. E. Direction-of-motion stereotypes: A review. *Ergonomics,* 1962, *5,* 357–383.

23. McCormick, E. J. *Human factors engineering.* New York: McGraw-Hill, 1964.

24. Miller, G. A., Heise, G. A., and Lichten, W. The intelligibility of speech as a function of the context of the test materials. *J. exp. Psychol.,* 1951, *41,* 329–335.

25. Morgan, C. T., Cook, J. S., III, Chapanis, A., and Lund, M. W. (Eds.) *Human engineering guide to equipment design.* New York: McGraw-Hill, 1963.

26. Rüedi, L., and Furrer, W. Physics and physiology of acoustic trauma. *J. Acoust. Soc. Amer.,* 1946, *18,* 409–412.

27. Spieth, W., Curtis, J. F., and Webster, J. C.   Responding to one of two simultaneous messages.   *J. Acoust. Soc. Amer.*, 1954, 26, 391–396.

28. Taubman, R. E.   Studies in judged number: I. The judgment of auditory number.   *J. gen. Psychol.*, 1950, 43, 167–194.

29. Taubman, R. E.   Studies in judged number: II. The judgment of visual number.   *J. gen. Psychol.*, 1950, 43, 195–219.

30. Thorndike, E. L., and Lorge, I.   *The teacher's word book of 30,000 words.*   New York: Bureau of Publications, Teachers College, 1944.

31. Welford, A. T.   *Ergonomics of automation.*   London: Her Majesty's Stationery Office, 1960.

index